10-Minute Critical-Thinking Activities for the World of Work

by

Ken Kaser

D1532168

J. WESTON
WALCH
PUBLISHER

Portland, Maine

User's Guide
to
Walch Reproducible Books

As part of our general effort to provide educational materials that are as practical and economical as possible, we have designated this publication a "reproducible book." The designation means that the purchase of the book includes purchase of the right to limited reproduction of all pages on which this symbol appears:

Here is the basic Walch policy: We grant to individual purchasers of this book the right to make sufficient copies of reproducible pages for use by all students of a single teacher. This permission is limited to a single teacher and does not apply to entire schools or school systems, so institutions purchasing the book should pass the permission on to a single teacher. Copying of the book or its parts for resale is prohibited.

Any questions regarding this policy or requests to purchase further reproduction rights should be addressed to:

Permissions Editor
J. Weston Walch, Publisher
321 Valley Street • P.O. Box 658
Portland, Maine 04104-0658

1   2   3   4   5   6   7   8   9   10
ISBN 0-8251-3823-X

Contents

To the Teacher

The activities in this book will help students develop the ability to think critically—a skill they will need for success in life and the business world. While it is human nature to simplify problems and experiences to make them easier to deal with, critical thinking avoids oversimplification. By completing the activities in this book, students will transfer their insights into new contexts. They will use their thinking skills and life experiences as well as their personal values and standards to find the best possible solutions. They will also distinguish between relevant and irrelevant facts and will learn to recognize contradictions. To think critically, students will consider strengths and weaknesses of opposing points of view, imaginatively put themselves in the place of others, and identify truth with their immediate perceptions or long-standing thoughts or beliefs. The chart on the next two pages correlates each activity in the book with the specific critical-thinking skills it fosters.

These activities focus on communication, prioritization, decision making, calculation, comprehension, and human relations skills. As they work through these activities, students will interpret evidence, statements, graphics, and questions. They will be given the opportunity to identify pro and con arguments for different situations. They will often be required to justify their answers and plans of action and to base their decisions on valid conclusions. Students will identify biases and assumptions that have influenced their final decisions.

The book is divided into four parts. Parts 1 and 2 consist of sets of related activities. Each activity can be assigned independently or in conjunction with the others in the set. The introduction to each section describes the thinking principles involved and briefly summarizes each activity.

The activities in this book are not sequential; that is, you may assign any activity at any time. Before assigning an activity it is recommended that you review it to determine whether the students would benefit from a warm-up discussion based on the elements involved, such as taxes and deductions, credit cards and credit limits, and so on. You may then want to reproduce the activity and distribute it to small or large groups or to the whole class, or you may prefer to make an overhead transparency for use with the entire class. If you divide the class into groups, the students will benefit from sharing their responses after the allotted time for discussion.

10-Minute Critical-Thinking Activities for the World of Work

ACTIVITY	Page	Logical Reasoning	Associative Thinking	Creative Thinking	Creative Fluency	Analysis	Critical Reading	Synthesis	Evaluation and Making Judgments
Utopia Department Store: Scenario 1	2	X	X	X	X	X	X		X
Scenario 1A	3	X	X	X			X	X	
Scenario 2	4	X	X	X		X	X		X
Scenario 2A	5	X	X	X		X	X		X
Paying for Road Repairs: Scenario 3	6	X	X	X			X	X	X
Scenario 4	7	X	X	X		X	X		X
Scenario 5	8	X	X	X		X	X	X	X
Scenario 5A	9	X	X			X		X	
Marketing the Special Occasions Hotel:									
Scenario 6	10	X	X	X		X	X		X
Scenario 7	11	X	X	X	X	X			X
Scenario 8	12	X	X	X	X	X	X	X	X
Pinstripes: Scenario 9	13	X	X	X	X	X	X		X
Scenario 9A	14	X	X	X	X	X	X	X	X
Scenario 10	15	X	X	X	X	X	X	X	X
One of the Three Certain Things in Life . . . :									
Scenario 11	16	X	X	X	X	X		X	X
Scenario 12	17	X	X			X	X	X	X
Scenario 13	18	X	X	X	X	X	X	X	X
Business Growing Pains: Scenario 14	20	X	X	X	X	X	X	X	X
Scenario 15	21	X	X	X	X	X		X	X
The Right Match for the Job: Scenario 16	22	X	X			X	X	X	X
Scenario 17	23	X	X			X	X	X	X
A Tempting Situation: Scenario 18	24	X	X	X	X	X	X	X	X
Scenario 19	25	X	X			X	X	X	X
Scenario 20	26	X	X			X		X	X
The Magic Transcript: Scenario 21	27	X	X			X	X	X	X
Scenario 22	28	X	X			X		X	X
Shopping the Net: Scenario 23	29	X	X	X	X	X	X		X
Scenario 24	30	X	X			X	X		X
Scenario 25	31	X	X	X		X	X	X	X

10-Minute Critical-Thinking Activities for the World of Work (continued)

ACTIVITY	Page	Logical Reasoning	Associative Thinking	Creative Thinking	Creative Fluency	Analysis	Critical Reading	Synthesis	Evaluation and Making Judgments
The Mistake That Was Found Too Late	34	X	X			X	X		X
Too Many Bosses	35	X	X			X	X	X	X
Promises, Promises, Promises	36	X	X	X	X	X	X	X	X
Working to the Beat of a Different Drummer	37	X	X			X	X		X
Fund-Raising That Is No Longer Fun	38	X	X	X	X	X	X	X	X
Avoiding the Clique	39	X	X			X	X	X	X
Overtime Bonanza	40	X	X	X	X	X	X	X	X
Team Spirit When Meeting Deadlines	41	X	X			X	X		X
Too Much Work, Too Little Time	42	X	X			X	X	X	X
Listen to Remember	43		X	X	X	X	X	X	
The Rule of 72 Makes Your Money Grow	44		X			X	X		
The Ugly American	45	X	X	X	X	X	X		X
Communications Breakdown	46	X	X	X	X	X	X	X	X
You Can Trust Me	49			X	X		X	X	X
Being Prepared with the Wrong Information	50	X	X	X	X	X	X	X	
Two Places at the Same Time	51	X		X	X	X	X	X	
Dealing with a Procrastinator	52	X	X	X	X	X	X	X	
Your Time on Company Time	53	X	X	X	X	X	X	X	
Suggesting Effectively	54	X	X	X	X	X	X	X	
Quantity, Quality, or Both?	55	X	X	X		X	X	X	
Taking Time Off	56	X	X			X	X	X	
Communicating Effectively with Your Audience	57	X	X	X	X	X	X	X	X
The Customer Is Boss	58	X	X	X		X	X	X	X
Hold the Phones: Telephone Etiquette	59	X		X	X	X	X	X	
The Right Place and the Right Time	60	X	X	X	X	X	X	X	X
Let's Do Lunch	61	X	X	X	X	X	X	X	
Breaking the Ice	62	X	X	X	X	X	X	X	

PART 1

This section includes five major scenarios, each split into mini scenarios.

Scenarios 1 and 2—Utopia Department Store

Scenarios 1 and 2 involve an upscale clothing store that offers different pay plans for full- and part-time employees. Students consider topics such as sales quotas, commissions, competition for customers, and employee stress as they analyze each situation to gain a better understanding of problems and opportunities. They will then interpret the situations, make decisions, and explain their decisions.

Scenarios 3, 4, and 5—Paying for Road Repairs

Scenarios 3, 4, and 5 involve raising taxes for the public good. Students consider several issues from the viewpoints of various citizens, including a state senator who wants to be re-elected. They discuss alternative taxes and fees as ways of raising money for road repairs. After considering the pros and cons of each solution, students make the best decision possible and determine how the decision affects the people involved.

Scenarios 6, 7, and 8—Marketing the Special Occasions Hotel

Scenarios 6, 7, and 8 examine the decisions a hotel manager must make to increase convention business. Students make decisions about a marketing campaign that aims at overcoming the drawbacks of weather, location, transportation, and competition. They also determine factors to consider when hiring a management team for the hotel.

Scenarios 9 and 10—Pinstripes

Scenarios 9 and 10 involve a successful clothing store that must decide whether to relocate or to lease more expensive space in the shopping mall where it is currently located. In these scenarios, students consider store investors' goals and determine which specialized departments to eliminate from the store and what special promotion will need to take place during remodeling. They also decide whether there are enough customers to support two stores.

Scenarios 11, 12, and 13—One of the Three Certain Things in Life: Taxes, Taxes, and More Taxes

Scenarios 11, 12, and 13 involve income taxes. Students examine voluntary compliance, progressive taxes, and following the rules set by government—issues that rarely excite workers. These issues become complicated when the natural tendency to rationalize is thrown into the mix. Students make decisions about paying social security taxes even when some predictions say that social security will not be available for their retirement.

Utopia Department Store

Scenario 1

Utopia is an upscale clothing store that carries the latest fashions for men and women. Utopia takes pride in the personal service it gives its customers. Many of the full-time salespeople have worked at Utopia for over 10 years and have regular customers who come into the store weekly. Salespeople are expected to sell $500,000 worth of merchandise each year, making their draw $42,500. Because sales in the clothing industry can be sporadic, depending on the season and holidays, Utopia pays full-time employees $3,541.66 each month, assuming their sales quotas will be met. When full-time salespeople do not meet their quotas, their October, November, and December paychecks are reduced accordingly. Salespeople who surpass their quotas are rewarded with larger salaries. Part-time salespeople are paid $5.50 per hour plus one percent on sales (before tax).

Items for Consideration

1. Why might Utopia pay part-time employees differently than full-time employees?

2. What is a salary draw? How is a salary draw a favorable or unfavorable way to pay employees in a retail clothing store?

3. Why do you think the full-time employees have remained loyal to Utopia for so long?

4. As a manager, what new incentives would you offer full-time and part-time employees to maintain the highest level of sales? Why?

5. Why might there be a conflict between the full-time and part-time employees in this situation?

Utopia Department Store

Scenario 1A

U topia pays full-time employees 8.5 percent commission on all sales. The following pie graph shows the five full-time employees' sales as a percentage of total sales.

UTOPIA ANNUAL SALES

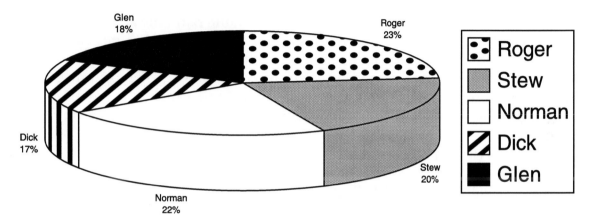

1. Utopia has total sales of $2.4 million for the year. Using the information in the graph, how much did each full-time employee sell?
   Norman: $ _____
   Stew: $ _____
   Dick: $ _____
   Roger: $ _____
   Glen: $ _____

2. Which employees seem to have the most loyal customer base? On what do you base your answer?

3. How much gross income did each full-time employee earn with an 8.5 percent commission on sales?
   Norman: $ _____
   Stew: $ _____
   Dick: $ _____
   Roger: $ _____
   Glen: $ _____

4. There is an opening for a new assistant manager. Based on the information in the pie graph, which of the current employees would you promote to this position? Why?

Utopia Department Store

Scenario 2

Utopia is an upscale clothing store that prides itself on the excellent service it provides. Like all clothing stores, it has busy and slow times. Slow times particularly affect the full-time employees, because much of their income is made up of sales commissions. (Part-timers receive an hourly wage as well as a much smaller sales commission.) Usually the men's department is staffed with one part-time and three full-time salespeople during the day and with two full-time and two part-time salespeople at night. Competition for customers' business is quite high, especially among the full-time salespeople. On slow days, as many as two or three full-time salespeople will ask to assist the same customer, which often causes frustration for all. Feeling uncomfortable with the competitive situation, many customers simply leave without buying anything.

Items for Consideration

1. List two problems mentioned in this scenario.

2. As a manager, what would you do to resolve the problem of overstaffing, keeping in mind that your store is successful because it gives individual attention to customers as well as excellent service?

3. Why are the full-time employees unhappy in this situation? What can be done to alleviate some of their unhappiness?

4. Are the part-time employees affected in this situation? How?

5. What would be an equitable formula for scheduling salespeople?

6. What kind of publicity for the store is created by this situation?

Utopia Department Store

Scenario 2A

Utopia recently conducted a survey of 100 top customers to determine their concerns with the store. The following graph shows the survey results.

Top Customer Concerns

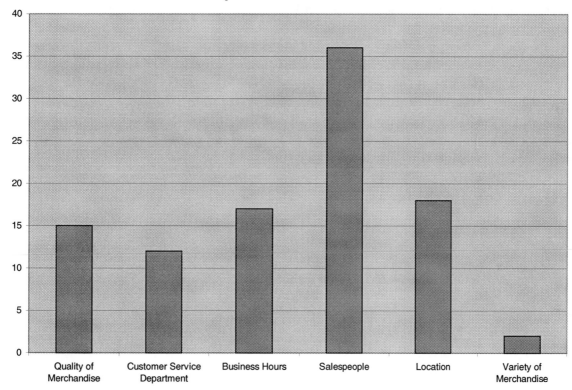

1. According to this graph, what is the top customer concern? After reading the scenario, what do you feel has contributed to this concern?

2. Which concern is the second highest in priority?

3. If you were the manager of Utopia, what changes or steps would you take to resolve each of the concerns in the chart?

4. Why is it important for Utopia to periodically take customer surveys?

Paying for Road Repairs

Scenario 3

State Senator Carole Green is concerned about the condition of roads in her sparsely populated state. A major highway that connects the eastern and western United States runs through the state. Federal funding for this highway has been cut, and the high volume of traffic has increased the need for expensive road repairs. The state collects money to pay for these repairs through an excise tax on gasoline and diesel fuel bought in the state.

Carlos, a major contributor to Senator Green's election campaign, is in favor of the excise tax on gasoline and diesel fuel. He feels that this method of collecting money is more equitable because it makes the people who use the roads responsible for the repairs. Carlos, however, does little traveling across the state.

Ron is a truck driver who feels that the excise tax unfairly targets the transportation industry. He believes that the gasoline and diesel fuel tax penalizes those who transport goods by road, because they purchase more fuel.

Items for Consideration

1. What is the major issue in this case?

2. Why is Senator Green concerned about the situation?

3. Is the excise tax on gasoline and diesel fuel to pay for repairs fair? Why or why not?

4. Why is Carlos in favor of the excise tax?

5. What would you do if you were Senator Green? Why?

6. What should Ron and other truck drivers do to try to change the current method of raising money to repair roads?

Paying for Road Repairs

Scenario 4

The roads in Senator Carole Green's state are badly in need of repair. However, the current practice of funding road repairs through a tax on gasoline and diesel fuel is not generating sufficient revenue. Many road repairs are postponed, sometimes indefinitely, making the roads potentially unsafe. Senator Green solicits and receives ideas from her constituents on how to generate the additional revenue needed to repair the roads.

Ron, a truck driver, has written to Senator Green. In his letter, he states that he does not want the excise tax on gasoline and diesel fuel to be increased; it is already 22 cents per gallon, the second-most-expensive tax of any state in the nation. Instead, Ron would like to see the state income tax raised, especially on higher incomes. This type of progressive tax would place more of the burden of repairing the roads on the wealthy, who have more income to spare.

Items for Consideration

1. What is the problem or challenge facing Senator Green in this situation?

2. What are three possible solutions for this problem or challenge?

3. What is a progressive tax? Would it be a good solution for the problem in this situation? Why or why not?

4. Why might Senator Green not choose to increase income taxes, especially on the wealthy?

5. If it were an election year, how might the senator's decisions be influenced?

6. What is the best solution for this problem? Why?

Paying for Road Repairs

Scenario 5

Senator Carole Green is studying ways to raise money for needed road repairs in her state. She is considering making the interstate highway that runs through her state a toll road. Each time a driver used the toll road, he or she would pay a fee. Because interstate traffic is so heavy, a toll road would raise a lot of money. Senator Green is also considering raising the state sales tax by one percent, which would be earmarked for road repairs. In this way, all purchasers in the state would share the burden of road repairs.

Items for Consideration

1. What are three alternatives for raising additional money to pay for road repairs? Who would be in favor of and against each possible solution? Why?

2. If you were the senator, what sources of information would you use to make your decisions? Who could give you the information you need? Why?

3. What is your solution to this problem? Why?

4. If you were Senator Green, would this solution help you get re-elected? Why?

Paying for Road Repairs

Scenario 5A

A toll road could provide much-needed funds for road repairs. The following chart indicates how many cars would use the toll road at different toll rates. Use the bar graph to answer the questions that follow.

Toll Rate	Charge per 10 Miles	Number of Cars Using the Toll Road per Month	Miles per Car	Total Revenue
1	$ 1.00	20000	20	$40,000
2	$ 2.00	15000	20	$60,000
3	$ 3.00	10000	20	$60,000
4	$ 4.00	8000	20	$64,000
5	$ 5.00	7500	20	$75,000

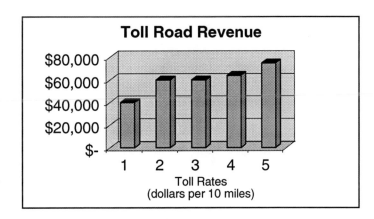

1. Which toll road rate appears to be the best revenue producer? Why?

2. What are the drawbacks of the best revenue-producing toll?

3. Name one advantage of the lowest toll rate.

4. What kind of toll rate would attract the most traffic?

Marketing the Special Occasions Hotel

Scenario 6

Georgia Jones is the director of marketing for the Special Occasions Hotel, a 300-room hotel/convention center. It is located in a growing Midwestern city with a population of approximately 200,000. The hotel has been completely remodeled. Additional convention space of 100,000 square feet and meeting rooms offering the latest technology are two highlights of the remodeling. A unique coffee shop and a four-star restaurant provide fine dining at the Special Occasions Hotel. Located downtown, the hotel offers ample parking, including a parking garage for guests. Three major airlines fly into the city, which is known for the warm hospitality of its people and its lively entertainment, including a children's zoo, a center for the performing arts, and a unique outdoor market that is open from May through October. The city also has an extremely low crime rate.

Items for Consideration

1. If you were the director of marketing for the Special Occasions Hotel, what five features would you emphasize to attract national business to your hotel?

2. What additional services could the hotel initiate to attract more conventions?

3. What are some of the drawbacks of this hotel/convention center? In what way are they drawbacks?

4. What kind of special promotions might attract national conventions to the Special Occasions Hotel?

Marketing the Special Occasions Hotel

Scenario 7

Georgia Jones, the director of marketing at the Special Occasions Hotel, is trying to attract more conventions to the hotel. She considers a competing hotel that captures a large percentage of conventions held in the area—the Supreme Convention Center, located 50 miles away in a city with a population of approximately 350,000 and an airport used by five major airlines. The city also offers many sources of entertainment, including a zoo, a center for the performing arts, and a minor league baseball team. However, this city has recently been experiencing a major increase in crime, and the Supreme is located close to areas where most of the crimes take place.

Items for Consideration

1. What additional challenge does the Special Occasions Hotel face, as indicated in this scenario?

2. List two advantages the Special Occasions Hotel has over the Supreme Convention Center.

3. What features of the Supreme Convention Center make it more attractive than the Special Occasions Hotel?

4. What features should Ms. Jones emphasize to attract conventions away from the Supreme?

5. Would it be ethical for Ms. Jones to advertise her hotel in a way that emphasizes the crime rate in the city of her competitor? Why or why not?

Marketing the Special Occasions Hotel

Scenario 8

Georgia Jones, director of marketing for the Special Occasions Hotel, faces the challenge of marketing a hotel/convention center located in a climate that has cold, snowy winters, rainy springs, and hot, humid summers. On the plus side, the newly-remodeled hotel offers prime convention space and meeting rooms equipped with the latest technology, as well as fine dining and ample parking. Further, it is located in a thriving midwestern city with a lively entertainment scene and a low crime rate. The city is also serviced by three major airlines.

Ms. Jones must determine how much to charge for hotel and convention space, and she must hire a winning team of managers to make the hotel/convention center a success. She knows she must compete with the Supreme, a nearby convention center, and offer convention planners a reason to choose the Special Occasions Hotel instead of the Supreme.

Items for Consideration

1. What kind of marketing campaign might attract business to the Special Occasions Hotel, despite the difficult climate?

2. What obstacles must Ms. Jones overcome?

3. What potential markets will Ms. Jones be targeting?

4. What qualities should Ms. Jones look for when considering prospective members of her management team? Where could she acquire names of prospective candidates?

5. What characteristics of the convention center should the marketing program highlight?

6. What methods should Ms. Jones use to inform prospective clients throughout the country about the Special Occasions Hotel?

Pinstripes

Scenario 9

Pinstripes is a successful specialty clothing store that has been in business for 90 years. The store, a family operation, is known for its specialized services to customers. Pinstripes grosses $2.5 million in sales annually. Twenty years ago, Pinstripes was at its peak, with three stores. Today Pinstripes has one store located in the only shopping mall in a growing Midwestern university town. The shopping mall, which was recently remodeled, is owned by a group of investors from another state. Space in the shopping mall rents for $40 per square foot. However, Pinstripes is locked into an old rental agreement for $14 per square foot. The store's owner has rented the same 2,500 square feet for the same low rate for the past 35 years. The lease is good for six more years.

Items for Consideration

1. Does Pinstripes have a successful track record? Explain.

2. What might have caused Pinstripes to downsize from three stores to one store?

3. Why might the new investors in the shopping mall not be enthusiastic about the Pinstripes store?

4. What factors must the owners of Pinstripes consider within the next 10 years if they want to be in business for the next 30 years?

Pinstripes

Scenario 9A

Pinstripes has been in business for a long time. The 2,500-square-foot store has bene-fited from an old rental agreement for $14 per square foot of store space. Soon Pinstripes will be faced with paying higher rent in the mall or finding an alternative location for the store. The following chart indicates all possibilities for this clothing store that makes $2.5 million annually.

Annual Rent for Pinstripes at Different Locations			
Location	Rent per Square Foot	Total Annual Rent	Percentage of Sales
Current Mall Today	$14.00	$ 35,000.00	1%
Current Mall Future	$40.00	$100,000.00	4%
New Mall Location	$30.00	$ 75,000.00	3%
Freestanding Bldg.	$28.00	$ 70,000.00	3%
Downtown Location	$25.00	$ 62,500.00	3%

Questions

1. How dramatic is the increase in rent at the current mall? Is it worth it to stay at the current mall where the customers are familiar with the location? Explain your answer.

2. Other than the rental cost, what would be the advantage of having a freestanding building?

3. What is the disadvantage of locating downtown in most large cities today?

4. If Pinstripes moves to a different location, what type of advertising or special promotions will be necessary to maintain customer loyalty? Why?

Pinstripes

Scenario 10

Pinstripes, a specialty clothing store, occupies 2,500 square feet of space in a mall that has recently been remodeled. Space in the mall rents for $40 per square foot, but Pinstripes has an old rental agreement for $14 per square foot. The lease expires in six years. The president of Pinstripes is Bob Massey, the grandson of the store's founder. Massey has been the manager of Pinstripes for the past 15 years. Because of Pinstripes' low rent, the owners of the mall have been pressuring Bob to split up the 2,500 square feet among several stores at a rent of $40 per square foot.

Bob faces many challenges as the manager of a local specialty store that competes with large national chain stores such as Macy's and Saks Fifth Avenue. He decides to remodel the store, which is 35 years old. Remodeling will take approximately two months to complete. Favorable relations must be maintained with the owners of the mall; however, remodeling must also be a top priority. Currently, Pinstripes leases out space to a shoe store, a tuxedo rental shop, an upscale gift shop, a famous college bookstore that also sells clothes primarily to college students, and a candy store. Bob must decide to which stores Pinstripes will continue to lease.

Items for Consideration

1. If you were Bob Massey, how would you determine to which stores to continue leasing space?

2. How can remodeling be accomplished without interrupting normal business?

3. Keeping in mind that Pinstripes' lease will end in six years, what costs of remodeling need to be considered?

4. Why is remodeling necessary, even though the lease runs out in six years?

5. What type of special promotion could take place during remodeling to avoid a decrease in sales?

6. What should Pinstripes' advertising emphasize to set it apart from its big competitors?

One of the Three Certain Things in Life: Taxes, Taxes, and More Taxes

Scenario 11

Bill Gold is employed part-time in the garden shop of a major retail chain, located in a rapidly-growing city. He works about 20 hours a week at the garden shop. The rest of the time he runs his own lawn-care service. Bill does all the work himself, and because of his fine work he has many loyal customers. At least 60 percent of Bill's customers pay cash for his services; the rest pay by check.

Bill does not believe that the federal government's tax system is fair to the working man and woman. He feels that the system favors the wealthy and puts the greatest burden on the middle-class taxpayer. Therefore, Bill feels that the less tax he pays, the more fair the system is for him. He has decided to report as taxable income only the payments he receives in the form of checks. He will not report any cash payments as income.

Items for Consideration

1. Would you classify Bill as an ambitious entrepreneur? Why or why not?

2. What do you think Bill is tempted to do in this situation?

3. The federal tax in the United States is a progressive tax. What is a progressive tax?

4. Should individuals like Bill take it upon themselves to make the tax system more fair from their viewpoint? Why or why not?

5. How is rationalization involved in this case?

6. Will the government have any record of Bill's cash earnings?

7. How should a self-employed person pay taxes during the year?

One of the Three Certain Things in Life: Taxes, Taxes, and More Taxes

Scenario 12

Shirley Gold works full-time as a hair stylist. She is paid a set salary plus a percentage of the hair care products she sells her customers. Shirley has many repeat customers who reward her with tips for a job well done. Most of her customers tip her in cash. Because the cash tips cannot be traced by the federal government, Shirley reports only a small percentage of her tips on her 1040 tax form.

Items for Consideration

1. Is it possible for the government to find out about Shirley's tips?

2. How is rationalization involved in this case?

3. Why should Shirley keep accurate records of all the tips she receives?

4. How is opportunity cost* involved in this case?

* Opportunity costs are resources given up when a choice is made. For example, a person has $30 to spend. That money can be spent on dinner for two, a new shirt, or a savings account deposit. If the person chooses to buy a new shirt, opportunity cost would be the dinner for two and the savings account deposit.

One of the Three Certain Things in Life: Taxes, Taxes, and More Taxes

Scenario 13

Bill Gold has a successful lawn-care business and a 20-hour-a-week job at a garden shop. Bill believes that the social security system will not exist by the time he is ready to retire. He feels that citizens should be allowed to save their own money for retirement instead of being required to pay social security tax from their income. He grudgingly accepts that social security taxes must be deducted from his paycheck from the garden shop. However, he does not pay social security on the income he makes from his lawn care service.

Bill's wife, Shirley, is a hair stylist. She does not report all her tips to the IRS. Shirley is concerned that the IRS will discover that she and Bill are not reporting all their income and that the government will expect Bill to pay social security tax on his lawn-care income. She raises this concern with Bill saying, "I worry that the IRS will audit our income tax returns. Your business has grown rapidly, and they might decide to trace all our earnings."

Bill reassures Shirley, saying, "How can the government keep accurate records on millions of people?" He goes on to say that records of cash payments cannot be traced and that even if the IRS catches on to him, he will be able to produce records of enough business expenses to offset any income received. Shirley accepts Bill's explanation but still worries that what they are doing is unethical and that an audit would result in hefty fines and a requirement to pay back taxes.

Items for Consideration

1. What is the rationalization in this case?

2. Instead of hoping that the government does not find out about Bill's lawn-care earnings, what should Bill and Shirley do? (Remember, Bill feels he can show enough expenses to offset income.)

3. Are Bill and Shirley's actions ethical? Are they legal? Why or why not?

4. Will Shirley also be in trouble if Bill's income tax return is audited, even though it involves his lawn-care business?

5. Do you believe that today's workers should be required to pay social security taxes even though this fund may run out by the time they retire?

6. What alternatives to social security might be possible?

7. Can individuals like Bill take it upon themselves to choose an alternative way to save for retirement instead of social security? Why or why not?

PART 2

Scenarios 14 and 15—Business Growing Pains

Scenarios 14 and 15 involve decisions that Marcella, a student and a successful entrepreneur, has to make regarding her growing business. Students will find these scenarios accessible because the key character is a teenager juggling school and a business venture.

Scenarios 16 and 17—The Right Match for the Job

Scenarios 16 and 17 place students in the role of a consultant making hiring decisions. Issues students evaluate involve leadership, favoritism, insecurity, networking, and decision making. Students will contrast logical decision making with decisions based on the "good old boy" system.

Scenarios 18, 19, and 20—A Tempting Situation

Discuss white-collar crime with the students before assigning Scenarios 18, 19, and 20, which involve ethics, honesty, integrity, and a worker's professional future.

An excellent computer programming student who also works as a department head at a hardware store decides to use his expertise in an unethical manner. Students will analyze the situations in the light of promotion, creditworthiness, ethics, friendships, and consequences of white-collar crime.

Scenarios 21 and 22—The Magic Transcript

Scenarios 21 and 22 involve friendship, ethically unsound choices, and one's professional future.

Scenarios 23, 24, and 25—Shopping the Net

These scenarios involve the growing use of the Internet for shopping, focusing attention on white-collar crime involving computers. Students analyze why the Internet is important to a retired couple. They interpret the downside of using a computer to purchase goods and analyze the issues of the credit card agreement versus the responsibilities of a credit card company.

Name_____ Date _____

Business Growing Pains

Scenario 14

Marcella is an excellent student who hopes to win a scholarship to a good school of culinary arts. A fine cook, she also provides baked goods three times a week to two supermarkets. Lately, individual customers have been asking Marcella to bake items for receptions and other special occasions. Marcella likes baking individual orders because she makes a greater percentage of profit than she does by selling larger orders to grocery stores. Time, however, is a scarce resource, and Marcella is quickly finding out that one person cannot do it all. Marcella's successful business has also taken a toll on her social life. She no longer has time to go out with friends and finds it increasingly difficult to relax. However, Marcella's savings account is growing rapidly.

Items for Consideration

1. What are two opportunity costs of running Marcella's baking business? (Opportunity costs consist of goods or activities not chosen or bypassed when a decision is made.)

2. What factor(s) has(have) made Marcella's business a success?

3. If you were Marcella, what would you do in this situation? Why?

4. In what way does Marcella's business benefit her the most?

5. What is the scarce resource in this case?

Business Growing Pains

Scenario 15

Marcella is a successful young entrepreneur. Her baking expertise could certainly earn her a lot of money for college. Marcella is happy about her income possibilities, but concerned about her lack of social life. Analyze the chart below to give Marcella sound advice for earning college money and having some social activity.

Income Possibilities for Marcella

Work Hours	Average Weekly Income	Average Annual Income
Work only weekends	$ 450.00	$ 5,400.00
Work 6 days per week	$ 600.00	$ 7,200.00
Work 7 days per week	$ 685.00	$ 8,220.00
Work 7 days per week/hire a second employee	$ 800.00	$ 9,600.00

Items for Consideration

1. Which option gives Marcella the greatest income? What are the advantages and disadvantages of this option?

2. What are the advantages and disadvantages of hiring a second employee?

3. What happens to annual income with a second employee? Where will some of that income be spent?

4. Which option do you think will give Marcella the best balance in life? Why?

The Right Match for the Job

Scenario 16

Neil Fortunato is the curriculum consultant for a large school district. He has been with the school district for 25 years. During these years he has held positions as social studies teacher, social studies consultant, and curriculum consultant. As curriculum consultant, Mr. Fortunato supervises 12 specialized consultants for social studies, business education, industrial education, family and consumer science, math, science, English, and special education. Each consultant is expected to demonstrate leadership in his or her specialty. Mr. Fortunato's responsibilities include ensuring that his department runs smoothly, instilling a sense of camaraderie among the consultants, and making decisions regarding curriculum for the district.

Mr. Fortunato particularly enjoys discussing academic philosophy and theory. He prefers discussion to decision making, which sometimes causes problems when difficult decisions must be made. Mr. Fortunato seeks the opinions of the specialized consultants through individual conferences and meetings. His leadership at these meetings can best be described as unstructured, loose, and lacking direction. His general leadership capabilities are weak, which is evident when consultants verbally attack each other during meetings.

Items for Consideration

1. How would you rate Mr. Fortunato as a leader? Why?

2. Which of Mr. Fortunato's characteristics indicate that he lacks leadership skills?

3. What kind of leadership style does Mr. Fortunato use: autocratic (heavy-handed), democratic (listens to everyone's ideas and then makes solid decisions), or open (has no apparent direction)? Give reasons to support your answer.

4. Would you enjoy working for Mr. Fortunato? Why or why not?

5. Could Mr. Fortunato's professional background limit his overall view of education? How?

The Right Match for the Job

Scenario 17

Neil Fortunato, the curriculum consultant for a large school district, was promoted to his current position by the school district's superintendent, May Jensen. Like Mr. Fortunato, Ms. Jensen enjoys discussing academic philosophy, and she surrounds herself with people who think as she does. Ms. Jensen is well liked and respected by the members of the school board, who trust that she will make sound promotion decisions.

Mr. Fortunato's background in social studies and his preference for other "academic" courses have made him unsympathetic to the need for such courses as business education, family and consumer science, and industrial education. Although he is the consultant for all areas of the curriculum, he is partial to social studies. Barry Giles, the district's consultant for business education, plans to retire at the end of the school year. Mr. Giles has been a strong advocate for business education. He believes that vocational courses are as important a part of a student's education as academic courses. Mr. Giles and Mr. Fortunato, his supervisor, often disagree about this issue.

Based on the district's finances, Mr. Fortunato has been asked to make budget cuts. He is thinking about changing the business-education consultant position. Mr. Fortunato is considering these options:
   (a) Keep the position as is and hire a new consultant to replace Mr. Giles.
   (b) Reduce the position to part-time, thus making it less powerful than the other consultants' positions.
   (c) Eliminate the position altogether.

Items for Consideration

   1. How was Mr. Fortunato promoted? Could this affect his hiring decisions?

   2. Networking involves associating and working with other professionals to enhance an individual's career opportunities. Is Mr. Fortunato's connection with Ms. Jensen an example of effective or ineffective networking? What makes it effective or ineffective?

   3. What are the advantages and disadvantages of each of the hiring options Mr. Fortunato is considering?

   4. Based on what you have read about Mr. Fortunato, which option do you think he will pick?

A Tempting Situation

Scenario 18

Bill Kurtz is a computer programming major at a community college. While attending college, he has been working as a salesperson in the hardware department of a major department store. Bill is very good at his job and has been promoted three times in two years. At age 20, he is the youngest department head in the store. Bill has also done very well at school. His internship in the computer program department at Bank One has gone so well that the bank has guaranteed him a job when he graduates from college. Bill is entrusted with many responsibilities both at the bank and in the hardware department.

Items for Consideration

1. What are Bill's greatest strengths?

2. Why do you think Bill has been promoted to department head at such a young age?

3. What is the advantage of having a successful business internship while attending college?

4. What marketable skills have led to much of Bill's success?

5. What might Bill's responsibilities at Bank One and at the department store include?

A Tempting Situation

Scenario 19

Bill is a computer programming major at a community college. He also works as a salesperson in the hardware department of a major department, store where he has been promoted to department head.

Bill has a credit card with a limit of $1,000 at the department store where he works. This is his first credit card, and he is enjoying the additional buying power it gives him. Bill has made some large purchases on his credit card and has reached his credit limit. Bill's friends, Preston, Tony, and Tina, also have credit cards from the store where Bill works. They come in often to shop when Bill is working.

Items for Consideration

1. What is one fringe benefit that Bill has received for working at the department store?

2. List three advantages and three disadvantages to using a credit card.

3. How has Bill managed his credit card? Explain.

4. What future problems may Bill encounter if he continues to use his credit card?

5. What advice would you give to Bill to ensure a successful financial and professional future?

A Tempting Situation

Scenario 20

Bill, a computer programming major at a community college, works part-time at a department store. As part of his studies, Bill also has an internship at Bank One. The bank has promised him a job when he graduates. Bill's proficiency with the computer allows him to get his work at the store done ahead of schedule. He often "plays" with the computers when his work is finished. He has found many loopholes in the store's accounting system. One slow day at work, Bill discovers how to access the accounts of credit card customers. He finds that it is easy to change account balances by keying in fictitious payments. Bill clears a large part of his credit card debt. He totally clears the accounts of his friends, who also have credit cards at the store. Bill's friends are pleased, but worry that he might be found out.

Bill tells his friends that no one knows about the loophole in the system and encourages them to make purchases with their credit cards. Bill wonders if the bank's computer system has a similar loophole.

Items for Consideration

1. Who are the participants in this case?

2. What is the dilemma in this scenario?

3. Is/are one or more people guilty of a crime?

4. What is likely to happen to Bill's future career?

5. What actions can the store take to prevent computer fraud?

6. What ethics are involved in this case?

7. What is Bill considering doing at the bank?

The Magic Transcript

Scenario 21

Denny is an outgoing, fun student. Unfortunately, he played too much during his freshman and sophomore years of college, and his 2.2 GPA is proof. Denny is currently enrolled in the College of Education with a major in social studies. The requirement for graduation with a teaching degree is a 2.5 GPA. Denny has the ability to do much better work. He started college with a Regent's Scholarship after being valedictorian of his high school graduation class. While he regrets not having taken his classes more seriously, he has been unable to raise his GPA to meet the requirements for a teaching degree.

Nancy met Denny at a student government meeting last year. Both are seniors and are active in campus organizations. They have become close, and are thinking about marriage. Nancy works part-time in the transcript office of the university. A trusted and valued employee, she has been placed in charge of updating grades on student transcripts. She really loves Denny and wants him to achieve his career goals. Lately, Denny has been hinting that Nancy could help him by changing the grades on his transcript to give him a more favorable GPA. Nancy wants to help Denny, but she is worried about doing something unethical. She is also afraid of what might happen if she gets caught.

Items for Consideration

1. What is Nancy's conflict of interest in this case?

2. What graduation requirement is Denny not meeting?

3. Why do you think the College of Education has this requirement for graduation?

4. Opportunity cost involves activities or goods that are bypassed when making one choice over other possibilities. What were Denny's opportunity costs during his freshman and sophomore years of college?

5. Instead of cheating, what could Denny do to achieve his goal of becoming a teacher?

The Magic Transcript

Scenario 22

Nancy and Denny are both seniors at Southern University. They are considering marriage. However, graduation is only a few weeks away, and Denny's GPA is too low for him to graduate with a teaching degree. He wants to graduate with Nancy so that they can pursue their future together.

Nancy works part-time in the transcript office of the university. It is her job to input students' grades on their transcripts. Denny has been pressuring her to change his grades.

One night Nancy agrees to stay late at work to input a backlog of grades. Because no one else is working late on this particular night, it would be the ideal time to put better grades on Denny's transcript. Nancy has already calculated that Denny needs three A's in place of D's to raise his GPA to 2.5. This would enable him to graduate with the teaching degree he so much wants.

Items for Consideration

1. What ethical dilemma does Nancy face?

2. What could happen to Nancy if she changes Denny's transcript?

3. Who is likely to discover the changed transcript first?

4. What is another way that Nancy could help Denny?

Shopping the Net

Scenario 23

Mr. and Mrs. Mann are a retired couple on a fixed income. They have become very proficient with the computer and have discovered ways to access many types of information. Lately, the Manns have been ordering merchandise over the Internet, using their credit card to pay.

The Manns are particulary fond of one site, Value Shop. Value Shop sells a variety of merchandise, including items from high-end stores such as Saks Fifth Avenue, Neiman Marcus, and Nordstrom. The Manns like this site because they can shop from their home by placing orders over the Internet instead of fighting traffic to get to the mall. The Manns trust Value Shop and are pleased with the quality of the items they have bought.

Items for Consideration

1. What is a limited resource for the Manns? Why?

2. What is a nearly unlimited resource for the Manns? What has this resource led them to do?

3. What are the advantages and disadvantages of using the computer to shop?

4. How might their approach to shopping keep the Manns from getting the best buys?

Shopping the Net

Scenario 24

Mr. and Mrs. Mann, a retired couple on a fixed income, often use their credit card to shop over the Internet. Unfortunately, another Internet user has acquired the Manns' credit card number. Their last credit card statement shows $800 in purchases that the Manns know they did not make. The statement shows that the purchases were made through Value Shop. Mrs. Mann calls Value Shop and finds that the merchandise was sent to several addresses in New York State. However, these addresses do not exist.

Mrs. Mann also calls their credit card provider to report the unauthorized purchases. She becomes extremely upset when the company refuses to remove the questioned charges from the bill. The credit card provider had sent its customers material urging them not make purchases over the Internet with credit cards because this can give unauthorized people access to credit card numbers. The credit card company claims that the Manns should have been aware of the dangers of purchasing merchandise over the Internet.

Many credit card providers send out newsletters encouraging customers not to give credit card numbers over the Internet. Using encrypted or secure Internet sites will decrease the amount of Internet fraud.

Items for Consideration

1. What consumer scams have taken place in this case?

2. Can the Manns be held accountable for paying the $800 worth of unauthorized credit card charges?

3. Does the credit card company's advice about Internet shopping suffice as a warning that the company will not hold customers exempt from fraudulent charges?

4. What dollar amount of unauthorized credit card charges can someone be held accountable for paying?

5. What could the Manns do in the future to protect themselves from fraud while continuing to shop over the Internet?

Shopping the Net

Scenario 25

Mr. and Mrs. Mann received a credit card bill with a charge of $800 for items they did not buy. Because the Manns often shop by credit card over the Internet, someone was able to access their credit card number and use it to charge the purchases. The Manns do not believe that they should be held liable for the charges. The credit card provider claims that they should have been aware of the dangers of shopping over the Internet. The Manns are angry that the credit company refuses to cancel the unauthorized charges. They decide to call the Better Business Bureau and the consumer editor of the local newspaper. While these express their sympathy, they can do nothing to help the Manns. Mr. Mann finally decides to make the matter public, so he calls the local TV station's consumer reporter. She reports the Manns' plight on the evening news, and the story is picked up by stations across the country. The credit card provider decides that the negative publicity is not worth the $800 in charges and removes the unauthorized charges from the Manns' bill.

Mr. and Mrs. Mann decide to do something to protect other consumers from such incidents. They write to Congressperson Joy Chen, asking her to help pass legislation that would regulate the methods by which purchases can be made over the Internet. Chen is sympathetic to their cause and wonders what she can do to help remedy the problem.

Items for Consideration

1. Did the credit card company fulfill its credit responsibilities in this incident?

2. What free consumer advocates did the Manns ask to help?

3. If you were Congressperson Chen, what would you do to limit such illegal activity on the Internet?

4. Is too much private information readily available on the Internet? If so, what can you do to prevent this type of incident from happening to you?

5. How do you think the Manns will make future purchases? Why?

PART 3

Scenarios in Part 3 enable students to analyze subjects like meeting deadlines, working effectively in a team, making promises, being on time, taking on too much responsibility, calculating numerical results, adjusting to another culture, and developing a market survey.

Scenario 26—The Mistake That Was Found Too Late

Students analyze a situation in which a valued employee makes a mistake that could cost the company a great deal of money. The brochures containing the mistake have been mailed to 500 customers. Students analyze the situation to gain an understanding of the consequences that can result from one mistake. They interpret possible results and explain their answers.

Scenario 27—Too Many Bosses

This scenario involves an employee who is torn between two employers. The employee is assigned more tasks than she can possibly handle. Students analyze the situation and decide the reason for the dilemma. They next explain what the employee can do to avoid similar dilemmas in the future.

Scenario 28—Promises, Promises, Promises

Scenario 28 involves a sales representative who is torn between filling a large new order and filling several earlier orders. Students examine the difficulty that arises from making promises that are hard to keep and how friendship can conflict with customer loyalty.

Scenario 29—Working to the Beat of a Different Drummer

Every business has its share of employees who are consistently late to work. This scenario involves an employee who justifies his tardiness by working late and who takes advantage of his friendship with his manager.

Scenario 30—Fund-Raising That Is No Longer Fun

In this scenario, students discuss an employee who continually tries to sell fund-raising items at work, focusing on how the fund-raising places other employees in an uncomfortable position. Students make decisions on how to end the fund-raising activities at work without upsetting the fund-raiser.

Scenario 31—Avoiding the Clique

Cliques are not just for teenagers—the workplace also generates cliques. This scenario involves the possible fallout from being inseparable friends at work.

Scenario 32—Overtime Bonanza

In this scenario, two employees handle overtime in two different ways, neither of them quite correctly. Students analyze the pros and cons of hiring more employees or paying more overtime.

Scenario 33—Team Spirit When Meeting Deadlines

This scenario involves the issues of perfectionism, time management, delegation of assignments, and handling the unexpected. Because a new computer malfunctions, an employee fails to meet a deadline. The points for discussion focus on the reaction of the person who delegated the responsibility and on what she can do to avoid similar problems in the future.

Scenario 34—Too Much Work, Too Little Time

Scenario 34 involves a highly qualified employee who is assigned more tasks than he can handle. Students formulate a plan to effectively handle diversified tasks.

Scenario 35—Listen to Remember

This activity involves most people's weakest communication skill—listening. The teacher reads a story to the students and presents them with nine true or false questions to evaluate their listening skills.

Scenario 36—The Rule of 72 Makes Your Money Grow

Students are given a limited time to put the Rule of 72 into action when calculating compound interest. Students also figure out what investments with a given rate of compound interest will be worth at different ages in a person's life. Students analyze different situations and calculate answers using the Rule of 72.

Scenario 37—The Ugly American

A global economy requires citizens of all cultures to know about other cultures. Special training can prepare Americans to handle international business more effectively. Americans are sometimes perceived as arrogant by people in other countries, who may call us "ugly Americans." Students determine what topics need to be covered in an international training seminar, and why.

Scenario 38—Communications Breakdown

Students analyze a situation in which the inability to speak or understand a foreign language creates a major challenge and determine the best way to handle it. Students also formulate strategies to avoid similar situations in the future.

The Mistake That Was Found Too Late

Scenario 26

You have worked at Mark Taylor Buick, a large new car dealership in Dallas, Texas, for six years. Because of your efficiency and accuracy, you have received three promotions. Your company is launching a sales promotion involving special General Motors financing for new Buicks, and Mark Taylor has asked you to design the brochure announcing the financing and mail copies to the dealership's 500 best customers within two days.

You have just sent the brochures to all key customers, along with a letter listing dates of special financing and payment plans for two-, three-, four-, and five-year sales contracts. You realize that two of the interest rates you listed in the letter are incorrect because you didn't get them from the latest General Motors report. Your promotional letter has made promises that General Motors does not intend to fulfill.

Items for Consideration

1. What factors contributed to the mistake made in this case?

2. What should you do first?

3. Should you inform your supervisor of the situation, even if you are sure you can resolve the problem by yourself?

4. How can you avoid this type of mistake in the future?

5. What extra costs might Mark Taylor Buick face because of your error?

6. Do you think it would be fair for Mark Taylor Buick to reprimand you for the mistake?

Too Many Bosses

Scenario 27

Shirley Baines is a secretary for a major local television network in San Diego. She handles work for both the president, Albert Lang, and the marketing director, Karen Ivers. Although Lang and Ivers work closely together, they don't check with each other when giving Shirley work assignments.

Albert Lang was made president because of his assertive nature and sound decision making. Much of his success can be attributed to the people he hires and delegates duties to. Mr. Lang is a demanding employer, but he lavishes praise on employees who do their jobs well. Karen Ivers, the marketing director, is an outgoing, friendly person who is fun to work with. She expects perfection from herself and her assistants, although she has a tendency to procrastinate. Shirley thoroughly enjoys working for Ms. Ivers but sometimes feels extra pressure to complete the tasks she assigns.

Shirley is a perfectionist who takes great pride in her work. She has a tendency to get frustrated if she feels the quality of her work is not up to the high standards she has set for herself. Most of the time Shirley can keep up with the work, but this morning Mr. Lang asked her to prepare an important contract by the end of the day, and then Ms. Ivers asked her to complete all the monthly sales reports by nine o'clock the next morning. It is impossible for Shirley to finish both jobs on time.

Items for Consideration

1. Describe Ms. Ivers's personality.

2. Why have Mr. Lang and Ms. Ivers become so dependent on Shirley?

3. How will Shirley probably handle the stress from this situation?

4. What effect might Shirley's personality and the demands of her supervisors have on her well-being?

5. In general, what can Shirley do to make sure that she is able to complete work assignments and meet deadlines set by both supervisors?

6. How should Shirley handle this particular problem? Why?

Promises, Promises, Promises

Scenario 28

Randy Allen is a sales representative for a major nursery in Florida. As part of his customer-contact program, he visits John Smith, the owner of a new home supply store in an area where many new houses are being built. John is very happy to see Randy, a good friend since college. John's store is having its grand opening in one week. John asks Randy to fully stock the garden center of the store in time for the grand opening. This will be a major order for Randy, who earns most of his salary through sales commissions. Randy knows that plant supplies at the nursery are limited. The only way he can supply enough plants to John is to deliver him three smaller orders already promised to other customers.

Items for Consideration

1. Why are sales representatives often paid a commission?

2. How is John abusing his relationship with Randy?

3. What decision should Randy make? Why?

4. What should Randy do to make all the customers in this scenario as happy as possible?

5. Why is it important for Randy to fill John's order?

Working to the Beat of a Different Drummer

Scenario 29

After completing their week-long training class, five new employees begin working in the customer relations department of a luxury hotel in Denver. Working hours are from 9 A.M. until 5 P.M., and lunch hour is from noon until one.

Glen, one of the new employees, is a friend of the hotel manager, Judy Lucero. Although Glen works until 5:30 or so on most nights, he generally arrives 10 to 15 minutes late each morning. Judy privately reminds Glen of the importance of arriving on time each day. Glen feels that Judy's comments are inappropriate, especially because on most evenings he works an extra half hour or so. Glen says to Judy, "Our friendship ought to be worth something."

Items for Consideration

1. Is Glen rationalizing his behavior? In what way?

2. Why should Glen know better than to arrive late for work?

3. What makes this situation difficult for Judy?

4. How do the other hotel employees probably feel about Glen's constant tardiness?

5. Is Glen justified in his thinking? Why or why not?

6. Does Glen's working later each day make up for his lateness each morning?

7. Is Judy justified in commenting on Glen's lateness?

Fund-Raising That Is No Longer Fun

Scenario 30

Carolyn Dinas supervises the advertising department of a major newspaper. In the past few months she has asked her co-workers to contribute to a variety of good causes. For example, she brought in candy her son was selling to raise money for new football uniforms, she took orders for her daughter's Girl Scout cookies, she asked for donations to support her church's building fund, and she sold raffle tickets for the Cancer Research Foundation. Some people were happy to contribute. Others felt that it was not appropriate for her to ask for contributions at work.

Items for Consideration

1. Who is Carolyn depending upon to support her special causes?

2. Why might employees in the advertising department feel extra pressure to support Carolyn's causes?

3. Which cause would the employees probably be happiest contributing to? Why?

4. What advice would you give Carolyn about her method of fund-raising?

5. Instead of relying on her co-workers, how might Carolyn raise money for worthwhile causes?

Avoiding the Clique

Scenario 31

Trent, Ben, and Antonia all started working at Brunswick Manufacturing at about the same time. They were in the same orientation group and liked each other immediately. Trent and Ben work in the sales department and Antonia is in the accounting department. The three usually have lunch together, go out together on Fridays after work, call each other, and drop by each other's offices several times a day. Sometimes they even get together on weekends. While Trent, Ben, and Antonia are lucky to have found such good friends at work, some of their co-workers are not as pleased about their close friendship.

Items for Consideration

1. What is the danger of becoming too friendly with co-workers or with socializing with them too much?

2. What objections might co-workers have to this three-person clique?

3. How can the three maintain their friendship without damaging their relationships with their co-workers?

4. Why is it important to have friends at work?

5. Some people think that the grapevine grows when one is socializing with co-workers. What does this mean?

Overtime Bonanza

Scenario 32

Saquib Doctor and Matt Waters work for Bluebird Nutrition, a vitamin packaging and distribution chain. Winter is the busiest season for Bluebird Nutrition. During the past three weeks, orders have been very heavy, and both Saquib and Matt have put in overtime. Bluebird Nutrition pays double for overtime hours.

Justin, their supervisor, is a cost-effective manager. He realizes that the busy season at Bluebird Nutrition requires overtime hours, but he also realizes that it does not make sense to hire additional employees because there will not be enough work for them during the slow seasons.

Saquib has been deciding for himself when he should work late. So far he has put in a total of 16 hours of overtime on four different days. He plans to give a listing of these hours to his supervisor, Justin, at the end of the pay period and ask for overtime pay.

Whenever Matt thinks that he should put in extra hours, he gets clearance from his supervisor first. Instead of receiving overtime pay, Matt plans to take an equal amount of time off at a later date. This time off is called compensatory time, or "comp time." Matt has accumulated 30 hours of comp time and plans to add three days to his vacation six months from now, although he hasn't told Justin yet.

Items for Consideration

1. Why doesn't Bluebird Nutrition hire more employees?

2. Which is more expensive for Bluebird Nutrition, overtime pay or compensatory time? Explain your answer.

3. Although Saquib and Matt both show a willingness to help by working overtime, both have also made mistakes in the way they are handling their overtime hours. What mistakes are they making?

4. What are some guidelines to follow when working overtime?

5. What policy could Bluebird Nutrition adopt to handle overtime more effectively?

Team Spirit When Meeting Deadlines

Scenario 33

At 4 P.M., Della gives Brenda a report containing some charts to be prepared on the computer. She tells Brenda that she will need the report for a meeting at 9:30 the next morning. Della is a perfectionist. She has always counted on Brenda to make her look good by finishing assigned projects neatly, accurately, and on time.

Two days ago, Brenda received a new computer with new software, which she has been learning during her few minutes of spare time. Brenda estimates that the job will take her about one hour to complete, so she decides to begin working on it when she arrives at 8:00 A.M. the next day. The next morning, Brenda's computer locks up halfway through the project. Brenda spends a lot of time studying the owner's manual in an attempt to resolve the computer problem, but she finally gives up and begins to look for a free workstation. By the time she finds one, it is 9:30. Della's meeting is about to begin.

Items for Consideration

1. Would Della be justified in telling Brenda that she is disappointed that the report isn't available?

2. What kind of in-service training would have been helpful for Brenda in this situation? Why?

3. Would Brenda be justified in saying that she was not to blame because she couldn't have known that the computer would malfunction?

4. How could this problem have been avoided?

5. In the future, what can Della do differently when assigning tasks?

Too Much Work, Too Little Time

Scenario 34

Kelvin was recently given a job in the marketing department of a nationally-recognized hotel/convention center. He was selected over several other applicants. Kelvin's supervisor has finished teaching Kelvin the basic responsibilities of the job, and she is beginning to give Kelvin more long-term projects to handle independently. Kelvin's job requires him to travel around the country to attract business to his hotel/convention center. Right now, in addition to his routine duties, Kelvin has a special mailing to get out by the end of the day, a report to write by tomorrow afternoon, a telephone survey to complete by the end of the week, a marketing plan to write by the end of next week, and a travel itinerary to develop for next month. As the number of assignments increases, Kelvin finds himself confused about what to do first and how to get everything done on time.

Items for Consideration

1. Why do you think Kelvin has been assigned so many varied tasks?

2. What are some extra pressures involved in traveling around the country?

3. Should Kelvin consult with his supervisor about his workload? Why or why not?

4. What should Kelvin do if it looks like he is going to miss a deadline?

5. Why is Kelvin willing to work so hard to make a good impression?

Listen to Remember

Scenario 35

Duplicate the questions below for each student, making sure that the story does not appear on the handout. Tell the students that you are going to read aloud a very short story. Encourage them to listen carefully because they are going to take a quiz about the story. When you have finished reading, distribute the questions. After they have answered the questions, encourage students to discuss their answers. When necessary, refer to the story to verify responses.

If students answer five or fewer questions correctly, their listening habits need work.

Mr. Ames, a banker, had just turned off the building lights when a taxi sounded its horn. Grabbing his briefcase, he ran down several flights of stairs and out into the street, waving frantically. No one was there, so he went to the nearest telephone to call a cab. He fished in his pockets, looking for a quarter.

Write True or False before each of the following statements.

1. The story has only one character.

2. The taxi's horn was not working.

3. The taxi came but left because no one was waiting outside.

4. The banker called a cab after he turned off the lights in the building.

5. The bank was a multistory building.

6. The banker had not brought his briefcase to work that day.

7. The executive's last name was Adams.

8. The executive was a man.

9. The executive planned to call the second cab from a pay telephone.

The Rule of 72 Makes Your Money Grow

Scenario 36

People invest money to make money. **Simple interest** is calculated on the basis of *principal* (the amount invested) times *rate* (annual percentage rate) times *time* (a year or a fraction of a year). **Compound interest** earns interest not only on the principal but also on the interest that is accumulating on the investment. Computer software programs make it easy to calculate what an investment earning compound interest will be worth in the future. However, the Rule of 72 provides a quick way to calculate how long it will take an investment earning compound interest to double in value. If you know the interest rate, dividing 72 by the rate will always give you the time it will take to double your investment.

How to Use the Rule of 72

Divide the annual interest rate into 72 and round to the nearest whole number. For example, if the interest rate is 8 percent, divide 72 by 8, which equals 9. It will take the investment nine years to double in value if the interest rate remains constant and no additional money is invested.

Items for Consideration

1. How many years will it take each of the following compounding investments to double?

   8 percent   12 percent   24 percent   4 percent   18 percent

2. Robert invests $4,000 at a compound interest rate of 12 percent. Robert is currently 30 years old. How much will his investment be worth when he retires at the age of 66?

3. Jennifer wants to be a millionaire when she retires. She has $5,000 to invest at a compound interest rate of 18 percent. Jennifer is currently 35 years old. At what age will she be a millionaire?

4. When investing money, would it be best to have interest compounded daily, weekly, monthly, or yearly? Why?

Name_____   Date _____

The Ugly American

Scenario 37

Pete works for a company that is involved in international business. Clients from other countries often visit the office, and many of Pete's co-workers have traveled abroad on business. Indeed, Pete hopes that in time he too will get a chance to travel. Last week he attended a company seminar titled "The Ugly American." The intent of the seminar was to make employees aware of appropriate and inappropriate behavior when dealing with people from other countries.

Items for Consideration

1. Why do you think the seminar was called "The Ugly American"?

2. If you were planning this special training seminar, what topics would you include? Why?

3. Why is it important for employees who travel abroad to attend this seminar?

4. What kind of assumptions might people in other countries make about visiting Americans?

5. Would it be valuable to have people from other countries speak at the training seminar? Why or why not?

Communications Breakdown

Scenario 38

You are sitting at the reception desk one morning when a client from Indonesia arrives to see Michele Carry, the sales manager. Michele has just called and told you that she will be 40 minutes late for the meeting. Michele, who is the only person in the company who speaks Bahasa Indonesia, told you that her client speaks very little English. She asked you to do your best to explain the situation to the client and to make her comfortable until Michele arrives.

Items for Consideration

1. How do you handle the situation?

2. What are some things you can do to make the client from Indonesia more comfortable?

3. If your company continues to increase its international trade and expects to have visitors from other countries, what things might be appropriate to have in the office reception area? Why?

4. If your company continues to increase its international trade, what in-service activities or special courses would help employees be good hosts to international clients?

5. What topics should be addressed at these special in-service activities? Why?

PART 4

Scenario 39—You Can Trust Me

Confidential information should not be shared with others no matter how much they pry. Students put themselves in the position of assistant to the president of a major corporation. The assistant knows information that must be kept confidential, even though another employee keeps asking questions. Students determine the best way to respond to the snoopy employee.

Scenario 40—Being Prepared With the Wrong Information

Sometimes the best laid plans can go awry. This scenario focuses on a person who goes to a meeting with the wrong report. Students analyze the situation, interpret the consequences, and explain how to rebound.

Scenario 41—Two Places at the Same Time

This scenario focuses on the issue of making too many commitments. An ambitious salesperson has appointments to meet two good customers at two different locations at the same time. Students analyze the predicament and discuss how to please all parties. They make recommendations on how to avoid similar conflicts in the future.

Scenario 42—Dealing With a Procrastinator

The world is full of procrastinators. Unfortunately, procrastination often causes problems for people other than the procrastinator, as this scenario illustrates. Students analyze the situation and explain what can be done to improve it.

Scenario 43—Your Time on Company Time

This scenario involves the improper use of a toll-free number at work. Students determine the ethical issue involved and give advice to the employee.

Scenario 44—Suggesting Effectively

This scenario involves a supervisor and an employee, both of whom are dissatisfied with each other. Students analyze the situation to determine what went wrong and develop criteria for better communication, successful completion of projects, and better employer/employee relations.

Scenario 45—Quantity, Quality, or Both?

This scenario focuses attention on quantity and quality. Students will analyze a situation about a well-liked, effective employee whose written communication almost always contains spelling errors. Students discuss the importance of accuracy in written communication and develop strategies to improve the situation.

Scenario 46—Taking Time Off

This scenario involves requesting specific vacation days at work. Students analyze a situation in which a valued employee who is rarely absent has legitimate reasons for wanting to take specific vacation days during the busy season. Students will recommend the best way to request time off and the best way for the manager to handle this situation.

Scenario 47—Communicating Effectively With Your Audience

In this scenario, an employee plans to ask the boss for a raise. Students determine the correct time to make the request, and why.

Scenario 48—The Customer Is Boss

This scenario involves an inattentive salesclerk who may be chasing business away. Students determine in what way the salesclerk acted improperly and suggest how similar incidents can be avoided in the future.

Scenario 49—Hold the Phones: Telephone Etiquette

Most customers can sense when a telephone operator is not particularly interested in being helpful. This scenario requires students to analyze a telephone conversation and determine what went wrong. Students are challenged to devise a training program on telephone etiquette that might include voice quality, attitude, and the appropriate questions to ask customers.

Scenario 50—The Right Place and the Right Time

It's fine to be friendly with co-workers. Unfortunately, some people socialize too much during working hours. This scenario involves a friend who ties up another friend's time at work. Students figure out how to maintain the friendship while decreasing the amount of socializing.

Scenario 51—Let's Do Lunch

While camaraderie in the workplace is important, it's also important to be aware of how one's choice of lunchtime companions might appear to others. Students figure out how to plan lunches to strengthen rather than fracture the work team.

Scenario 52—Breaking the Ice

Students analyze a typical business setting and plan a luncheon for new employees.

You Can Trust Me

Scenario 39

As the assistant to the president of a major corporation, you are aware of a lot of confidential information. The personnel director recently resigned, and another employee is trying desperately to find out who the next director will be. You know who will be named as the new director.

The curious employee has tried to pry information out of you with such statements as these:

"You have a really important position. I'm sure you know who the new personnel director will be."

"The person who used to have your job would have told me what was going on."

"If you tell me, I won't tell anyone else. I promise."

Items for Consideration

1. Respond to each of the curious employee's statements.

2. Should you reveal the new personnel director's name?

3. How could revealing the name hurt or help you in the organization?

4. Why do you think the curious employee is so intent on finding out the name of the new personnel director? If you told this employee, do you think that he or she would really keep the information a secret?

Name_____ Date _____

Being Prepared With the Wrong Information

Scenario 40

Luke Ortiz works in the sales department of Flynn's Furniture. His supervisor asked him to attend a meeting with the advertising department. His supervisior wants Luke to explain how the two departments can work together more effectively to increase sales. Luke misunderstood the subject he was to discuss; he has prepared a talk on the function of the sales department. As he listens to his supervisor's introduction, Luke realizes his mistake.

Items for Consideration

1. What would be the consequences for each of the following actions:
   a. Luke gives the report he prepared.
   b. Luke admits his mistake and asks to have the meeting rescheduled.
   c. Luke blames his supervisor for giving him the wrong information.
   d. Luke bluffs his way through his presentation and hopes that no one notices.

2. How could this situation have been prevented?

3. What alternatives might there be to rescheduling the meeting?

Two Places at the Same Time

Scenario 41

You are a sales representative for a large manufacturer. You are very good at managing your time and take pride in getting a lot done in a short time. You are visiting Charles Marshall, the purchasing agent for a prospective client. You have been trying for eight months to convince Mr. Marshall to purchase from your company because you know it could be a very profitable account. Mr. Marshall has finally placed a sizable order with you. Because it is almost lunchtime, he suggests that the two of you eat together. However, you have an appointment with Sally Hirschhein, a longtime customer whom you have been trying to develop into an even larger account. It will take you approximately 45 minutes to travel to your appointment.

Items for Consideration

1. Suggest ways in which you can make your important second call without antagonizing Mr. Marshall.

2. Why is it important to go to lunch with Mr. Marshall?

3. Why is it important to be on time for your appointment with Ms. Hirschhein?

4. How can you prevent this situation from happening again?

5. Why do clients like individual, undivided attention?

6. How has your greatest asset become a drawback in this case?

Dealing With a Procrastinator

Scenario 42

Mickie works as a budget clerk in the accounting department at the University of Nebraska. She is in charge of managing the money for several research projects and special curriculum projects at the university. Each month Mickie prepares budget statements for these projects and distributes them to the appropriate researchers. The researchers are supposed to review the statements, verify their accuracy, and return them to Mickie so that she can prepare her monthly report.

For the last three months, one of the researchers, Dr. Reed, has been consistently late in returning his approved statements to Mickie. Mickie has sent Dr. Reed written reminders asking him to return the statements to her by a certain date, but Dr. Reed waits until the last minute to submit the statements to her. As a result, Mickie has had to complete her last three monthly reports on the same dates that they were due.

Items for Consideration

1. What can Mickie say to Dr. Reed to get him to submit his approved statements to her on time?

2. If Mickie doesn't think that Dr. Reed will ever be on time, what can she do individually with him to avoid personal frustration?

3. Whose problem has Dr. Reed's procrastination become?

4. What could Mickie do to make Dr. Reed respond more quickly to her requests?

5. Do you know someone who is a procrastinator? How do you deal effectively with this person?

Your Time on Company Time

Scenario 43

Desmond Rhodes works in the customer service department of Career Paths, a large professional-development company. This company sells videos and holds seminars on professional development and improvement. Desmond answers inquiries coming in on an 800 number and makes many monthly long distance calls. During his breaks, he sometimes uses the company telephone to call members and friends who live in other parts of the country. He has also given the company's 800 number to several friends, who call him occasionally. Desmond's friends like the convenience of using the 800 number to call their old friend. Besides, it doesn't cost them anything. Desmond feels that it is all right to use the telephones in this way because the company is paying for these services.

Items for Consideration

1. Is Desmond stealing from the company? Explain.

2. If Desmond is an outstanding worker, could long-distance calls made on the company telephone be considered a fringe benefit of his job?

3. How might Career Paths find out about Desmond's improper use of the telephone?

4. What might be the consequences of Desmond's improper use of the company telephone?

5. What advice would you give Desmond about making personal long-distance calls from a work phone? Write this advice in the form of a dialogue between Desmond and you.

Suggesting Effectively

Scenario 44

Willie Chao is an experienced clerk in the accounting department of Younker's Department Store. He has received many awards for his good work. Last week his supervisor, Charlotte Clifford, asked him to research the cost of recarpeting the entire store. She wanted to have the report on her desk by Thursday morning. Willie worked hard on the project and stayed late to complete it on time. When Charlotte saw the report, she complained that Willie had included information on only three carpet suppliers, that he hadn't presented the figures in the format she wanted, and that he had wasted time researching useless information about carpet pads. Both Willie and Charlotte were unhappy with the outcome of the assignment.

Items for Consideration

1. What specific questions could Willie have asked Charlotte before starting work on the project?

2. Why does Willie feel wronged in this situation?

3. What lesson should Charlotte learn from this experience?

4. Why might Charlotte have assumed that Willie needed no additional instructions for this assignment?

Quantity, Quality, or Both?

Scenario 45

Trevian Mathis works as an assistant to Joan Smith, sales manager for Contact Tour and Travel Agency. Contact Tour and Travel does a lot of business in the Washington, D.C., area. Some of its major clients include politicians, foreign dignitaries, and CEOs. Many of these clients ask for Trevian because they like his outgoing, friendly, and helpful personality.

Joan is in the process of preparing Trevian's first performance appraisal. In Joan's opinion, Trevian has many obvious assets, including his expertise and excellent productivity. One serious flaw in Trevian's performance is that virtually every letter, memo, or other piece of writing he prepares has one or more spelling errors—and Trevian's job requires a lot of writing.

In a meeting with Trevian to discuss his performance, Joan comments on Trevian's poor spelling and points out that this flaw mars his otherwise good performance.

Items for Consideration

1. What is Trevian's deficiency in this case?

2. How can this deficiency be turned around?

3. What are five of Trevian's top professional characteristics?

4. How should Trevian respond to Joan's comment?

5. Why is it important for Trevian to improve his spelling?

Taking Time Off

Scenario 46

Oriana Chavez works in the sales division at Success Plush, a Boulder, Colorado based wholesaler of stuffed animals and toys. Her department is under a lot of pressure to fill the holiday orders for this year's hot toys. All orders must go out no later than November 15. Oriana is aware that the two months before major holidays (such as Christmas, Hanukkah, Valentine's Day, and Mother's Day) are the busiest times for Success Plush. Flora Occhino, the general manager, has asked all employees to take off as little time as possible during the next few months. She has been checking attendance records and vacation requests very carefully.

Oriana has just lost a cap on one of her teeth and will have to take time off to go to the dentist. In addition, her brother is being married in another state the second week of November, and Oriana wants to take several days' vacation to help with arrangements and attend the wedding. Oriana's family from Nebraska is coming to Boulder the first weekend of November, and Oriana would like to take a few days off days to spend with her family. During her three years with the company, Oriana has taken only five vacation days and one sick day. She has an exemplary attendance record and has accumulated 45 vacation days.

Items for Consideration

1. List three of Oriana's strongest assets in this job.

2. Does Oriana have legitimate reasons to be absent from work?

3. What can Oriana do to minimize the disruption her absences will cause and avoid making herself look bad in Flora's eyes?

4. Why should Flora give special consideration to Oriana's requests for time off?

Communicating Effectively With Your Audience

Scenario 47

When communicating orally or in writing, you need to take your audience into account and plan when and how to deliver your message. How can you tailor the message so that it will have the effect you want?

Matt Brown is planning to ask his supervisor, Jason Anderson, for a raise. Matt has recently taken on more responsibility and feels he deserves more money.

Matt is aware that Jason is very busy preparing for the annual sales meeting. Matt has observed that Jason always insists that employees follow established company procedures. Jason likes to carefully study all the facts in a situation before making a decision. Matt knows that Jason suspects that he is looking for another job. However, this is not true; Matt wants to stay in his current position.

Items for Consideration

1. What can Matt do to maximize his chances of getting a raise?

2. Given Jason's decision-making style, what would be the best way to approach him for a raise?

3. Should Matt reassure Jason that he is not looking for another job?

4. When would be the best time to approach Jason about a raise?

5. How could Matt find out what the company policy is regarding raises?

6. If Matt is not successful in getting the raise he wants, what should he do?

The Customer Is Boss

Scenario 48

Robert Lovelace and Stuart Edwins are salesclerks at an upscale men's clothing store. Robert works part-time at the checkout counter and is paid an hourly wage. Stuart sells clothing. He is a full-time employee and is paid commission for his sales.

One evening a customer approaches Robert and asks where the Giorgio Armani suits are located. Robert is busy talking to his wife on the telephone and pauses just long enough to point and tell the customer, "Over there." The customer says something to Stuart about Robert's lack of willingness to be more helpful. The man, who happens to be one of Stuart's best customers, patronizes the store because it gives good personal service.

Items for Consideration

1. What customer expectation is Robert not meeting?

2. Why should Stuart talk to Robert about this situation?

3. Should Stuart talk to Robert in private or in public? Why?

4. Could Robert's actions be excused if it had been an unusually busy day and this was his only chance to take a personal break? Why or why not?

5. Why did the customer feel short-changed in this situation?

Hold the Phones: Telephone Etiquette

Scenario 49

The following telephone exchange between a caller and the telephone operator took place at a large company.

Operator: Hello?

Caller: Who is this?

Operator: To whom do you want to speak?

Caller: I was trying to reach someone in the personnel department.

Operator: This is the personnel department.

Caller: Is Shirley Stetson there?

Operator: Yes, she is.

Caller: May I speak with her, please?

Items for Consideration

1. Why might the caller in this situation become frustrated?

2. What telephone rules need to be taught to the telephone operator?

3. Could this telephone conversation (possibly long-distance) be made shorter? How?

4. Rewrite the conversation, keeping in mind efficiency, politeness, and the caller's needs.

5. What should this company include in a telephone etiquette training plan?

The Right Place and the Right Time

Scenario 50

Your good friend and co-worker Carlotta is in the habit of stopping by your office unannounced to discuss personal matters, sometimes two or three times a day. Although you enjoy talking with Carlotta, you find her interruptions disruptive and time-consuming. Because of them, you sometimes have to take work home, which allows you less time to spend with your family.

You have made several unsuccessful attempts to tell Carlotta that you enjoy her visits but that you are swamped with work.

Items for Consideration

1. What delicate situation exists here?

2. How could you tell Carlotta that you need more uninterrupted work time without hurting her feelings?

3. What are the conflicting issues in this case for you?

4. What is the opportunity cost when you spend work time visiting with Carlotta?

5. How can you continue visiting with Carlotta without having to take work home?

Let's Do Lunch

Scenario 51

You might not think that anyone cares with whom you have lunch, and you might feel that lunchtime has nothing to do with how you do your job. But look at the lunch habits of three employees at First Capital Investments.

Michael Jones works as a telemarketer. He never eats lunch with anyone from the office. Becky Mock is a financial assistant to three stockbrokers. She has lunch every day with Andrea Williams, another financial assistant in the same department. They never ask anyone else to join them. Alex Gains is a stockbroker who sometimes eats with other stockbrokers and sometimes with people from other departments. Occasionally his supervisor joins him for lunch in the company cafeteria.

Items for Consideration

1. What are the advantages of having lunch with co-workers in your department?

2. What are the advantages of having lunch with workers in other departments?

3. It is human nature to develop "grapevines" at work. What might co-workers think when they see Alex having lunch with his supervisor?

4. What is the advantage of not eating lunch with anyone? What is the disadvantage?

5. How could the whole company become a more tightly-knit operation through some type of lunchtime function?

6. How could the employees in this company function more as a team?

Breaking the Ice

Scenario 52

Shakeila Crisswell has been asked to serve as host at a luncheon for new employees to be held in the company dining room. There will be approximately 25 guests at the luncheon, including five new employees.

Items for Consideration

1. Name three things that Shakeila can do to make the new employees feel at ease.

2. What can Shakeila do to get people to mingle and not just gather in their comfortable, established groups?

3. What should Shakeila hand out to guests as they arrive at the luncheon to help them get acquainted?

4. What activities at the luncheon might help break the ice?

5. What makes the difference between a rigid business atmosphere and a more comfortable and productive atmosphere?

6. What preparations should Shakeila make to introduce the newcomers to the other attendees?

Answers

Part 1

Utopia Department Store

Scenario 1 (p. 2)

1. Utopia wants to make sure that full-time employees perform to their maximum potential. Being paid a commission will encourage full-time employees to work very hard for sales. Part-time employees will not always work during the busiest time of day and they will be competing directly with full-time salespeople. It is unfair to base their pay only on commissions.

2. A salary draw is a predicted amount that full-time salespeople earning a commission will make. An estimated amount is paid each month to full-time employees, which gives them a more consistent income. At the end of the year, salaries are adjusted up or down according to the real commission earned.

3. The full-time employees have probably remained loyal due to stable commissions and a salary draw that makes monthly income more predictable.

4. Possible new incentive may include bonus pay for selling a certain dollar amount on weekends or a given day. Employees could also receive a bonus for selling the most of a certain clothing item. Time off and extra vacation time may also be used as incentives for reaching sales quotas. Pay raises and greater employee discounts could also be used as rewards.

5. The full-time employees may be very territorial with sales and their customers since commission puts more pressure on them to produce. The full-time employees may resent successful part-time employees. The part-time employees may feel that they are being pushed around by the full-time employees.

Scenario 1A (p. 3)

1. | Norman | $528,000 | $2.4 million × .22 |
   |--------|----------|---------------------|
   | Stew | $480,000 | $2.4 million × .20 |
   | Dick | $408,000 | $2.4 million × .17 |
   | Roger | $552,000 | $2.4 million × .23 |
   | Glen | $432,000 | $2.4 million × .18 |

2. Roger, Norman, and Stew seem to have the most loyal customer base because they have the greatest percentage of total sales.

3. | Norman | $44,880 | $528,000 × .085 |
   |--------|---------|-----------------|
   | Stew | $20,800 | $480,000 × .085 |
   | Dick | $34,680 | $408,000 × .085 |
   | Roger | $46,920 | $552,000 × .085 |
   | Glen | $36,720 | $432,000 × .085 |

4. Answers will vary. Probably the employees with the highest sales (Roger, Norman) should be considered first for promotion. Their sales indicate loyalty to the company.

Scenario 2 (p. 4)

1. Two problems in the situation include (a) too many sales people going after the same customer and (b) competition between full-time and part-time employees becoming too aggressive, since the full-timers have a lot of pressure to produce.

2. The manager could track sales records for each day of the previous year to determine staffing needs this year. Employees should follow the rules "First salesperson to greet the customer waits on the customer. If the customer requests another salesperson, the requested salesperson helps the customer."

3. Full-time employees depend totally on commission. They are unhappy with competition from part-time employees. The manager can do a better job of scheduling to alleviate some tension. Full-time employees could be given the options of commission or salary plus commission.

4. Part-time employees are affected in this situation by being less likely to make sales, which equals less income. Part-time employees are also receiving a lot of pressure from full-time employees.

5. The manager should monitor when the greatest sales take place and split up the time equitably among full-time employees. Part-time employees should also be scheduled equitably. Part-time employees could be challenged with contests offering rewards as certain sales goals are reached.

6. When salespeople treat each other rudely, the customer is uncomfortable and usually leaves the store without buying. The overzealous employees fighting for customers give the store bad publicity.

Scenario 2A (p. 5)

1. The top customer concern is salespeople (37%). Overzealous salespeople fighting for customers have caused the concern.

2. The second highest concern is location (18%).

3. As manager, I would make sure that the store continues to carry the highest quality, guaranteed merchandise . The customer service department would periodically have staff development to improve customer relations. I would conduct a customer survey from the numerous customers in our computer system to determine what hours are most convenient for shopping. Salespeople would be given staff development to improve image and teamwork. If the store is very successful, I would consider opening a second location near the customer base. Variety of merchandise seems to be a strong point. I would make sure our buyers keep the store stocked with clothing to meet our customer needs.

4. Customers are the reason a store exists. Feedback on surveys from customers will help the store improve sales and/or satisfy customers.

Paying for Road Repairs

Scenario 3 (p. 6)

1. The major issue is financing highway repairs.

2. State Senator Green represents the people in her state. Repairs to the highway represent a financial challenge to the state. Some type of tax will have to pay for repairs.

3. Excise tax on gas and diesel fuel is fair from the viewpoint that people who drive pay for the roads. It is unfair from the viewpoint that people not driving on the highway and not paying excise taxes may still benefit from the road.

4. Carlos is in favor of the excise tax because it does not directly affect him.

5. Answers will vary. This is an opinion question.

6. Ron and the other truck drivers should lobby state senators to find other financial means to repair the highway.

Scenario 4 (p. 7)

1. Senator Green must come up with additional funding to repair highways in her state.

2. Raise excise taxes on gas and diesel fuel. Use higher income taxes to repair roads. Raise sales tax on all goods and use a percentage to repair roads. Change the highway to a toll road where all users are charged a fee.

3. A progressive tax has an increased rate as income increases. Repair of roads should not necessarily be paid by higher income taxes. People making higher incomes should not pay a heavier tax burden for road repair.

4. Senator Green may have wealthy constituents who contribute to her campaign. She does not want to lose the votes of these constituents.

5. If it were an election year, the Senator might make a decision that is more likely to gain her votes.

6. Answers will vary. Raise excise taxes: People need to purchase fuel and this money will pay for the road. Raise income taxes: People earning higher incomes are more capable of paying the taxes to repair the road. Increase sales tax: Use a percentage of the sales tax for road repair. Change the road to a toll road: The people using the road actually pay for it.

Scenario 5 (p. 8)

1. Alternatives—Toll road: Everyone pays who uses the road. People who rarely use the road would be for this proposal and frequent travelers on the interstate would be against this proposal. Sales tax: Nearly everyone who makes purchases within the state would be unhappy with additional sales tax. People just using the highway and not making purchases within the state would be happy. Excise tax on gas to repair roads: People who use a lot of gas would be unhappy and persons rarely buying gas would be happy.

2. I would go to the bureau of statistics to determine how much money the sales tax would generate. I would go to the department of roads to determine how much traffic uses the

highway and to determine how much money would be generated from a toll. I would check appropriate sources to determine how much gas is sold in the state each year when considering an excise tax on gas.

3. Answers will vary. The toll road directly charges persons using the road. The sales tax placed the road repair burden on all citizens who make purchases in the state. The excise tax once again targets persons who drive.

4. The toll road may or may not help me get re-elected. Most people are not excited about stopping and going on a major highway to pay a toll. Even more people would be upset with sales tax increases.

Scenario 5A (p. 9)

1. The $5 rate produces the greatest total revenue ($75,000).

2. The best revenue-producing toll has the smallest number of cars using the toll road per month.

3. The lowest toll rate serves the greatest number of cars.

4. The $1 rate attracts the most traffic (120,000 cars per month).

Marketing the Special Occasions Hotel

Scenario 6 (p. 10)

1. Answers will vary: hotel facility, accessibility to airport (with three major airlines), four-star restaurant, remodeled hotel with additional space and latest technology, entertainment, hospitality

2. free shuttle service to and from airport, free morning newspapers, special weekend rates, computers in hotel room, special room service, breakfast buffet included with the room

3. The size of the city may be too small. Only three airlines may be too limiting. Weather in the Midwest during the winter is not attractive for convention business.

4. Special weekend package including breakfast buffet, specials on meeting rooms (no charge for meeting room rent) when also purchasing a catered meal, complimentary rooms for conventions renting large numbers of rooms, special introduction to people planning convention meetings (a free meal, one night's lodging for free if they book the convention at our hotel)

Scenario 7 (p. 11)

1. The Supreme Convention Center is located in a larger city with more airport service. Special Occasions Hotel is in a city with fewer entertainment options.

2. less crime, better location

3. larger airport, larger city with more entertainment possibilities

4. safe, clean city, four-star restaurant, ample parking, newly remodeled facility complete with technology

5. Ms. Jones could emphasize the safety of her city without emphasizing the crime rate around the Supreme Convention Center.

Scenario 8 (p. 12)

1. The marketing theme should focus on positive aspects of the hotel. Newly remodeled facility, latest technology, excellent food, plentiful parking, low crime rate, entertainment, and accessibility to three airlines should be emphasized in the marketing campaign.

2. Ms. Jones must overcome challenging weather, a strong competitor (the Supreme), and fewer airlines (3) into the city.

3. Ms. Jones should target markets that would appreciate a safe, clean city with the latest up-to-date facilities and technology. She probably will target people in the Midwest who are used to the climate. Ms. Jones will go after conferences that will not require over 300 rooms.

4. outgoing, knowledgeable about conventions, good presenters and negotiators; university placement offices, colleagues in the hotel industry

5. The marketing program should highlight the newly remodeled facility, latest technology, and the four-star restaurant and coffee shop.

6. Internet, convention publications, national newspapers, brochures sent to national and local organizations that meet annually, have a booth at major convention trade shows

Pinstripes

Scenario 9 (p. 13)

1. Being in business for 90 years indicates success; however, going from three stores to one does not indicate success.

2. too much competition, not keeping up with the latest trends, decrease in sales

3. The new investors will not be thrilled with earning $15 per sq. ft. instead of $40 per sq. ft.

4. Pinstripes must consider a new location since their lease expires in six years. They need to consider an up-to-date marketing mix to deter further downsizing.

Scenario 9A (p. 14)

1. The increase in rent is nearly 186%. It may be worth looking into alternative locations which cost $25,000 to $37,500 less per year than the new rate for the current mall.

2. A freestanding building has its own parking lot.

3. Many downtowns no longer have much retail to attract customers. Also parking is very limited in downtown areas.

4. Have a grand opening sale, send out coupons to customers, give free coffee/cookies for the grand opening, and hold a drawing for a free wardrobe. Why: This will give customers a reason for continuing their business instead of going to a competitor.

Scenario 10 (p. 15)

1. Bob should give the highest priority to stores that attract the most customer traffic. These stores also mean more business for Pinstripes.

2. Remodeling can take place in sections so the store will not have to close. Possibly remodel ¼ or ⅛ of the store at a time.

3. When spending great sums of money on remodeling, Bob Massey must consider if the store will remain in the mall after the lease is up. Will remodeling be a cost-effective move? Will the remodeled store mean more sales?

4. Remodeling is necessary because customers are not attracted to an outdated store.

5. Pinstripes could have special remodeling sales while the remodeling takes place.

6. Pinstripes should emphasize that it is a specialty store different from most department stores. Also Pinstripes should emphasize its 35-year commitment to the community.

One of the Three Certain Things in Life: Taxes, Taxes, and More Taxes

Scenario 11 (p. 16)

1. Bill is an ambitious entrepreneur because he works at more than one job and his customer base is growing.

2. Bill is tempted to avoid taxes by not reporting cash payments he receives.

3. A progressive tax charges a greater percentage of taxes to higher income levels.

4. Individuals should not cheat the tax system because they believe it is more fair for them. They should contact their elected representatives to change the tax system.

5. Bill rationalizes that it is OK to do something illegal to make the tax system more fair for him.

6. The government may have a record of Bill's cash earnings if his customers write off his services on their income tax forms.

7. A self-employed person should pay estimated taxes quarterly to avoid a big burden at the end of the year.

Scenario 12 (p. 17)

1. When the government learns of Shirley's job, they will be expecting higher tips reported. If the IRS audits Shirley's taxes, she must show records of tips.

2. Shirley rationalizes that the government won't be able to track her cash tips, so she decides not to report this income.

3. Accurate records will be necessary if the IRS does a tax audit.

4. Shirley bypasses paying taxes now, but this may result in greater future penalties.

Scenario 13 (p. 18)

1. The rationalization in this case is that social security won't exist in the future; therefore, it's OK to not pay into it now.

2. Bill should report his income and expenses correctly to the government. If he has enough expenses to offset income, he should fill out the tax form accordingly.

3. Their actions are not ethical or legal. U.S. citizens are expected to pay income taxes. This is called voluntary compliance. Bill and Shirley's actions are not ethical because they are cheating the government (other citizens).

4. Shirley will also be in trouble since they file a joint return as a married couple.

5. Answers will vary. Either pay social security taxes or be required to put money into a retirement fund for the future.

6. Alternatives include investment funds, pensions matched by employers, and tax-sheltered annuities.

7. Social security still exists and Bill must contribute fairly to the system.

Part 2

Business Growing Pains

Scenario 14 (p. 20)

1. social life, leisure time, relaxation

2. excellent baked goods, reliability, consistency

3. Answers will vary. Continue the baking business to earn more money for college. Cut back on business to maintain high grades and earn scholarships.

4. Marcella's business gives her excellent experience in the culinary arts and business management. It also earns money for college.

5. Time is the scarce resource in this case.

Scenario 15 (p. 21)

1. Work seven days per week/hire a second employee. Advantages of this option are greater income and more visibility in the business world. Disadvantages include no social life, little time for studies, and little time for relaxation.

2. The second employee will cut down Marcella's work load and enable Marcella to bake more. Disadvantages to a second employee include less net income and an assumption that the second employee will take the same kind of pride in the business as Marcella has demonstrated.

3. Annual income goes up. Some of that income will be spent on the second employee's salary.

4. Marcella may want to work only on weekends, making a respectable income. This plan will give her more time for studies, social life, and relaxation.

The Right Match for the Job

Scenario 16 (p. 22)

1. Poor. He has a hard time making decisions. He can't run a meeting where participants respect each other.

2. Neil has a hard time making difficult decisions. He cannot run a smooth meeting.

3. Neil uses open or no leadership. He has no sense of direction, which leads to arguments and confusion among his employees.

4. Answers will definitely vary (personal opinion).

5. Mr. Fortunato has a social studies background. This may limit his perspective of other academic areas. He is more into philosophy than reality.

Scenario 17 (p. 23)

1. Mr. Fortunato was promoted by someone who has the same academic philosophy as his philosophy.

2. Ineffective networking: Networking in this situation is based totally on similar viewpoints and represents little growth. This networking situation is more of a friendship and not a professional growth strategy.

3. a. The budget is not cut. Business education still has a position of equality with other academic areas.

   b. The budget is reduced and business education is still somewhat represented. Business education has less power.

   c. Business education will not receive favorable representation. The budget will be cut.

4. Mr. Fortunato will choose (b) or (c) since his philosophy does not favor business education.

A Tempting Situation

Scenario 18 (p. 24)

1. responsible, good grades, trustworthy, computer background, successful internship

2. Bill has demonstrated skill, responsibility, and computer expertise. His successful internship helped him obtain the job.

3. The internship is a good time to prove your capabilities.

4. computer literate, experience with computers, proven sales success

5. Bill might be more responsible for computer programming in the hardware store and the bank. He might also have leadership responsibilities as a department head.

Scenario 19 (p. 25)

1. credit card

2. Advantages: more buying power; buy now, pay later; take advantage of sales. Disadvantages:

interest, temptation to buy more than you need, higher prices

3. poorly: He has charged the card to its limit.

4. Bill may have a hard time paying the credit card off.

5. Do not charge more than you can pay off in several months. Only purchase items that you really need. Don't let credit problems mess up your business and personal life.

Scenario 20 (p. 26)

1. Bill, department store, Bill's friends

2. Bill is tempted to use the computer illegally to steal from the department store.

3. Bill and his friends are guilty of a crime. The friends who do not stop Bill's actions are just as guilty as Bill for theft.

4. Bill's future career is in severe jeopardy. If the bank finds out what he has done, he will lose a successful career.

5. The employees enter a code and all transactions are traced back to individual employees.

6. Theft, computer fraud

7. Bill is considering defrauding the bank, a heavily regulated business.

The Magic Transcript

Scenario 21 (p. 27)

1. The conflict is her ethical job responsibilities vs. love for Denny.

2. 2.5 GPA

3. Teachers need to demonstrate academic strength with sound grades.

4. Denny has played during college. His opportunity costs are respectable grades and loss of scholarship.

5. Denny could take extra courses, study, and improve his GPA.

Scenario 22 (p. 28)

1. The ethical dilemma is changing grades illegally to help Denny graduate.

2. Nancy could jeopardize her graduation and her reputation for honesty.

3. Denny's college advisor or the transcript review department (for graduation purposes)

4. Nancy could help Denny settle down and study to earn higher grades.

Shopping the Net

Scenario 23 (p. 29)

1. Income: The Manns are retired.

2. Time: Extra time has enabled the Manns to become proficient with the computer and shopping over the Internet.

3. Advantages: don't have to leave home, easy to order merchandise. Disadvantages: sharing credit card over the Internet, will constantly be hounded by possible sales over the Internet, wrong people get hold of your credit card number

4. Just using the Internet means less comparison shopping takes place. This may prevent the Manns from getting the best buy.

Scenario 24 (p. 30)

1. Credit card fraud, Internet fraud

2. Yes—If they cannot prove that someone else illegally made the charges. They may be accountable for $50 of charges.

3. No

4. $50

5. Pay by means other than credit cards.

Scenario 25 (p. 31)

1. Yes, they remove the charges.

2. BBB, newspaper, local television station's consumer reporter

3. Fine companies that accept illegal charges from stolen credit-card numbers.

4. Yes. Be careful not to supply too much personal information over the Internet.

5. Not over the Internet. This negative experience will dampen their use of shopping over the Internet.

The Mistake That Was Found Too Late

Scenario 26 (p. 34)

1. not verifying GM rates before finalizing the brochure (efficiency but not accuracy)

2. All 500 customers must be notified of the mistake. The supervisor and GM should also be notified.

3. The supervisor needs to know the mistake and your solution. The supervisor needs to be able to respond correctly to customer concerns.

4. Take more time to verify accurate information.

5. Lost customers, additional money spent on postage to send out a new mailing, offering other financial incentives/rewards to the 500 customers.

6. A reprimand may be appropriate since this is a serious mistake.

Too Many Bosses

Scenario 27 (p. 35)

1. Ms. Ivers is a perfectionist who procrastinates. Her procrastination puts pressure on co-workers.

2. Shirley is dependable and she is a perfectionist.

3. Shirley will have to choose one project over the other. This puts unwarranted pressure on Shirley. She will have to let one of her employers know that his/her project is not first priority.

4. Shirley's personality and the demands of her supervisors may cause stress and ulcers for Shirley.

5. Shirley should not overbook her work schedule. She needs to be honest with her supervisors concerning what is possible and what is not.

6. Shirley will have to be honest with both supervisors. She will need more time to get both projects done.

Promises, Promises, Promises

Scenario 28 (p. 36)

1. Sales representatives are paid commission as an incentive to sell more.

2. John is depending on a friend to fulfill his last-minute needs.

3. Randy should not deprive the three original customers of their orders because they are expecting the orders as agreed upon. Randy must tell John that he cannot fulfill the order due to short notice.

4. Randy should fulfill the original customers' needs first and then supply Dave with the remaining inventory, promising to fulfill an additional shipment as soon as possible.

5. Randy will benefit from the sales of a new customer. It is a potentially profitable addition to his customer base.

Working to the Beat of a Different Drummer

Scenario 29 (p. 37)

1. Yes. Glen assumes that his friendship with the manager and staying late at work should allow him to arrive late to work.

2. It should be common sense to arrive to work on time.

3. This is a difficult situation for Judy because she is Glen's friend.

4. Other employees probably resent Glen's tardiness.

5. No. You are expected to be on time to work.

6. No. Glen must fulfill his scheduled hours.

7. Yes. Judy is the manager responsible for overseeing her employees.

Fund-Raising That Is No Longer Fun

Scenario 30 (p. 38)

1. Carolyn is depending on co-workers to support her special causes.

2. Fellow workers may feel pressure to contribute in order to keep their supervisor happy.

3. Raffle tickets for the Cancer Research Foundation (This cause is not so specialized and it funds a serious threat to life.)

4. Carolyn should keep community fund raising separate from work. Constantly asking for money may cause hard feelings at work.

Avoiding the Clique

Scenario 31 (p. 39)

1. Too much socialization at work may result in poor production.

2. Co-workers may feel alienated by the clique. They may be suspicious or jealous that they're not included in the group.

3. The three can maintain their friendship more outside of work hours.

4. It's important to like the people at work. It makes the job more pleasurable.

5. The grapevine involves rumors and speculations. When relationships become too close at work, rumors and speculations tend to grow.

Overtime Bonanza

Scenario 32 (p. 40)

1. Bluebird doesn't hire more employees because there will not be enough work to keep them busy during the slow season.
2. Overtime pay costs more than compensatory time. Compensatory time means time off, which costs a company the regular rate of pay.
3. Saquib should get clearance first from Justin to work overtime. Matt should let Justin know that he plans to take comp time.
4. When working overtime, make sure to get approval from the supervisor first. Overtime work must be productive to be cost-effective.
5. Bluebird could adopt a policy of no overtime or a limited amount of overtime that must be approved first by the supervisor.

Team Spirit When Meeting Deadlines

Scenario 33 (p. 41)

1. Yes. If Della does not realize Brenda's computer challenges, she is justified in telling Brenda that she is disappointed. Brenda could have started the project the previous day. After all, she knew that the computer would present challenges.
2. Computer/software in-service. Brenda deserves training about the new computer and software that she is expected to use effectively.
3. It is true that Brenda could not predict the computer malfunction; however, she should have allowed more time for the project.
4. This problem could have been resolved with appropriate training and development. Also an extra computer with the original software would be helpful.
5. Della should allow more time for projects.

Too Much Work, Too Little Time

Scenario 34 (p. 42)

1. Kelvin has been assigned a lot of tasks because the supervisor believes he can handle the ambitious schedule.
2. Traveling around the country produces jet lag and it causes work to pile up at home.
3. If Kelvin is totally overwhelmed by the number of jobs, he could ask his supervisor for suggestions.

4. If Kelvin feels that he will miss a deadline, he should let his supervisor know.
5. Kelvin wants to prove to the company and his supervisor that he was the best choice for the job.

Listen to Remember

Scenario 35 (p. 43)

1. True
2. False
3. True
4. False
5. True
6. False
7. False
8. True
9. True

The Rule of 72 Makes Your Money Grow

Scenario 36 (p. 44)

1. 8% = 9 years
   12% = 6 years
   24% =3 years
   4% = 18 years
   18% = 4 years
2. $256,000
3. At age 67, you will have $1.28 million.
4. You want money to compound interest daily to earn more.

The Ugly American

Scenario 37 (p. 45)

1. Americans are referred to as being ugly if they assume that the rest of the world must be dictated by American standards.
2. Culture—You never cut a business deal if you aren't willing to learn the culture. Customs—Respect customs important to others. Business practices—How are business practices different from the practices in the U.S.? Food—What unusual foods will you encounter in the other country?
3. The seminar will help you prepare for a successful trip.
4. Americans are arrogant. Americans think that their way is the best. Americans assume everyone speaks English.

5. Yes. It is good to have viewpoints from other countries.

Communications Breakdown

Scenario 38 (p. 46)

1. This is a delicate situation. The explanation requires simple English.
2. Offer the guest coffee or a soda. A magazine or newspaper may come in handy; however, keep in mind that the client speaks little English.
3. Dictionaries for translation to avoid uncomfortable situations due to communication breakdowns
4. The in-service should include the importance of respecting other cultures, learning about other cultures, and using a translation dictionary.
5. Topics should include coping with differences in customs, language, and communication.

You Can Trust Me

Scenario 39 (p. 49)

1. "Thanks for the compliment, but the importance of my position has no bearing on knowing the new personnel director."
   "You are referring to prior practices, but we are not allowed to share confidential information."
   "*Confidential* means I can't even tell you."
2. No
3. By prematurely divulging the new personnel director's name, you could stir up conflict and confusion within the company. You will also prove that you are untrustworthy and unable to perform your job effectively.
4. This employee wants to butter up the person in charge of hiring. He/she will not keep the information "secret."

Being Prepared With the Wrong Information

Scenario 40 (p. 50)

1. (a) If Luke gives the report he has prepared it will not match the reason for the meeting. (b) Time is limited and all participants may be upset about attending an additional meeting. (c) It doesn't accomplish anything trying to blame someone else. Luke should not try to embarrass his supervisor. (d) Usually persons

in an audience can tell when someone is not amply prepared.
2. Luke should have verified the meeting date and topic with his supervisor well in advance of the meeting.
3. Perhaps Luke could present information about the sales department and ask persons from the advertising department how the two departments can work more effectively as a team. This brainstorming session could be used to formulate ideas that Luke sends to all participants as a summary memorandum.

Two Places at the Same Time

Scenario 41 (p. 51)

1. Call Sally to see if she can meet later and you will purchase dessert. Be honest with Mr. Marshall that you appreciate the opportunity to have lunch, but you have another appointment. He will appreciate your loyalty to the long-time customer. Ask Mr. Marshall if you can meet for lunch the next week.
2. Mr. Marshall is a prospective large account.
3. Ms. Hirschheim has been a dedicated customer for a long time.
4. Next time make sure to allow a large enough window of time for each appointment.
5. Clients appreciate having the full attention of a sales representative. It makes them feel important.
6. Time is your greatest asset; the limited amount of time in this case has become a drawback.

Dealing With a Procrastinator

Scenario 42 (p. 52)

1. Mickie can let Dr. Reed know that if he is late with his verification, he will receive late payment, perhaps even a month late.
2. Mickie can give Dr. Reed an earlier deadline and then when he is late, she will actually have the information on time.
3. Dr. Reed's procrastination has become Mickie's problem.
4. Mickie might send copies of her reminders to Dr. Reed's supervisor. If Dr. Reed realizes that several people are tracking his procrastination, he may change his late ways. Mickie can give Dr. Reed an earlier deadline to outwit his procrastination.

5. Answers vary due to personal opinion requested.

Your Time on Company Time

Scenario 43 (p. 53)

1. Yes. Desmond is stealing telephone time from the company. The company pays for the 800 number based on telephone usage.

2. No. Long distance phone calls at no charge are normally not a fringe benefit. Desmond should not reward himself with a fringe benefit.

3. Career Paths will receive telephone records showing calls placed and calls received.

4. Desmond may lose his job due to his actions.

5. You: Aren't you concerned about getting caught making long distance calls at work?

   Desmond: It's an 800 number and the company receives a greatly reduced rate.

   You: Each call still costs the company.

   Desmond: They owe it to me because I work long, hard hours.

   You: If you continue making long distance calls, you will jeopardize your job.

Suggesting Effectively

Scenario 44 (p. 54)

1. Willie should have asked Charlotte specifics about the carpet project.

2. Willie worked hard on three proposals and he is probably upset that Charlotte is not satisfied with his work.

3. Charlotte should learn from this experience that she needs to give more specific instructions to be fair to her co-workers.

4. Charlotte has always depended on Willie's experience and she probably assumed that he would see the project from her perspective.

Quantity, Quality, or Both

Scenario 45 (p. 55)

1. Failure to proofread, resulting in misspelled words on correspondence the office sends

2. Trevian should use spell check and grammar check on the computer. He should take time to proofread.

3. expertise, productivity, outgoing, friendly, helpful

4. Trevian should acknowledge the problem and pledge to do better in the future.

5. Correct spelling is very important for business correspondence. It tells a lot about the company sending the correspondence.

Taking Time Off

Scenario 46 (p. 56)

1. exemplary attendance, dependable, years of experience

2. yes

3. Oriana can volunteer to work overtime and weekends to make up for the time she will be gone.

4. Oriana's exemplary attendance record and unique circumstances deserve special consideration from Flora.

Communicating Effectively With Your Audience

Scenario 47 (p. 57)

1. Matt can make a special effort to follow Jason's procedures. Matt should carefully prepare his presentation for effectiveness. Matt should approach Jason when Jason is in a good mood and under less pressure.

2. Jason should plan his presentation. Approach him at a time when there is less pressure.

3. Matt should assure Jason that he is not looking for another job if the topic arises.

4. Matt should approach Jason after the annual sales meeting.

5. Matt could consult the employee handbook or call the human resources department to learn about the policy on raises.

6. Matt should ask Jason what he can do to improve his chances for a raise. Also he should keep alert to other job opportunities.

The Customer Is Boss

Scenario 48 (p. 58)

1. Undivided attention to the customer

2. Stuart wants to maintain good customer relations. He can also help Robert avoid being unsuccessful with customer relations.

3. Stuart should talk to Robert in private because it is a personal issue.

4. No. If Robert is taking a personal break, it should not be on the sales floor.

5. The customer did not receive good service.

Hold the Phones: Telephone Etiquette

Scenario 49 (p. 59)

1. The person answering the telephone is using poor telephone etiquette.

2. The operator needs to be taught telephone etiquette, clarity, and helpfulness.

3. Yes. The person answering the telephone is causing the call to drag out due to poor etiquette.

4. Operator: Hello, Brunswick Corporation, this is Karen. How may I help you?

   Caller: May I speak to Shirley Stetson in the personnel department?

   Operator: I will connect you to Shirley's extension.

The Right Place and the Right Time

Scenario 50 (p. 60)

1. The delicate situation is a choice between completing work and possibly hurting a friend's feelings.

2. Ask Carlotta if you could share a conversation during break or lunch. Let Carlotta know that you have an appointment.

3. Conflict between work and friendship

4. The opportunity cost is not completing work and having to take it home.

5. Visit during breaks or lunch.

Let's Do Lunch

Scenario 51 (p. 61)

1. It establishes a positive camaraderie for the workplace.

2. Diversity and different perspectives are good for the soul.

3. Rumors might have Alex buttering up his supervisor.

4. An advantage is that you can get more work done and avoid the company grapevine. The disadvantage is segregation and co-workers feeling that you are not sociable.

5. Periodically a company lunch activity would be good to strengthen relationships.

6. Periodically the company could have interdepartmental meetings so all employees gain a better understanding of the total operation.

Breaking the Ice

Scenario 52 (p. 62)

1. Introduce new employees to others. Break the ice and make them feel at home. Make sure the new employees have an enjoyable time.

2. Ice-breaker activities can successfully establish more conversations. Seating arrangements at the table can be very effective at breaking up cliques.

3. Shakeila could hand out name tags and a listing of all employees.

4. Get-acquainted activities or games can break the ice. Have participants introduce one another.

5. an agenda, time for introductions, time for brainstorming, time for breaks

6. Shakeila should learn something about each new person to share with the rest of the people at the meeting.

Share Your Bright Ideas with Us!

We want to hear from you! Your valuable comments and suggestions will help us meet your current and future classroom needs.

Your name_____Date_____

School name_____

School address_____

City _____State _____Zip_____Phone number (_____)_____

Grade level taught_____Subject area(s) taught_____Average class size_____

Where did you purchase this publication?_____

Was your salesperson knowledgeable about this product?   Yes_____   No_____

What monies were used to purchase this product?

____School supplemental budget   ____Federal/state funding   ____Personal

Please "grade" this Walch publication according to the following criteria:

Quality of service you received when purchasing .... A   B   C   D   F
Ease of use... A   B   C   D   F
Quality of content.. A   B   C   D   F
Page layout .... A   B   C   D   F
Organization of material .... A   B   C   D   F
Suitability for grade level .... A   B   C   D   F
Instructional value... A   B   C   D   F

COMMENTS:_____

_____

What specific supplemental materials would help you meet your current—or future—instructional needs?

_____

Have you used other Walch publications? If so, which ones?_____

May we use your comments in upcoming communications?   ____Yes   ____No

Please **FAX** this completed form to **207-772-3105**, or mail it to:

   Product Development, J. Weston Walch, Publisher, P. O. Box 658, Portland, ME 04104-0658

We will send you a **FREE GIFT** as our way of thanking you for your feedback.   **THANK YOU!**